AA

Roadsi...s
& Truckstops

CREDITS

Produced by AA Publishing.
Text, photos and site locations supplied by
MC Handbooks Limited © 2005.
© Design and cartography by Automobile
Association Developments Limited 2005.
Automobile Association Developments
Limited retains the copyright in the current
edition © 2005 and in all subsequent
editions, reprints and amendments to editions.

Advertisement Sales: advertisingsales@theAA.com
Editorial: lifestyleguides@theAA.com

Cover pictures courtesy of Ace Cafe London
& Roger Tuson/The Rider's Digest

The Automobile Association wishes to thank the following picture
libraries for their assistance in the preparation of this publication.
AA World Travel Library Back cover top (James Tims), Back cover
bottom (James Tims), 1 (Steve Watkins), 2 (Steve Watkins), 8 (Chris
Coe)DigitalVision 6tPhotodisc 6b, Photograph of Sally Boazman
reproduced with the permission of BBC Photo Library.

Typeset/Repro by Maple Print Basingstoke

Printed by Graficas Estella, S.A., Navarra, Spain

Published by AA Publishing which is a trading name of Automobile
Association Developments Limited whose registered office is
Fanum House, Basingstoke, Hampshire, RG21 4EA
Registered number 1878835.

CIP catalogue record for this book is available from the British Library

ISBN-10: 0-7495-46751
ISBN-13: 978-0-7495-4675-5

A02594

Ordnance Survey® This product includes
mapping data licensed from
Ordnance Survey® with the
permission of the Controller
of Her Majesty's Stationery
Office. © Crown copyright
2005. All rights reserved.
Licence number 399221.

Maps prepared by the
Cartography Department of
The Automobile Association.
Maps © Automobile
Association Developments
Limited 2005.

CONTENTS

Trucking Around?

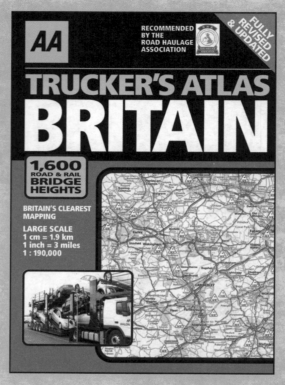

Long haul, short haul you'll be lost without the AA Truckers Atlas

Foreword
by Sally Boazman

Many years ago, I worked in a very small office, compiling and reading traffic reports for the AA.   A few of us crammed into a little office, and with the help of AA patrol cars and local police, built up a picture of where jams, queues and delays were causing the most problems. These were the first real traffic reports anywhere in the country, and I suppose in our way, we were pioneers of a sort; there was no fancy equipment, no cameras to see the roads, and certainly no drivers with mobile phones to phone us and tell us where the jams were. But between us, we started a bit of a trend.

Driving, back then, could be a lonely old business; Anyone who spent time driving around the country had very little information to help them dodge jams or roadworks. Not only was traffic news in short supply, but there wasn't much in the way of other information, apart form the wonderful AA Handbook, which, one way or another, found it's way into most people's glove boxes. There really were very few facilities that catered solely for motorists' needs, and what there was was, at best, expensive and scarce.

Winding on a few years, I now find myself at Radio Two and things are very different; traffic is more stressful, there's more congestion, and we all travel further. So we need as much help as we can get! I try and do my bit by telling you where the jams are – and here are the AA, doing their bit by compiling a wonderful book for everyone who drives and who, occasionally, needs to stop and rest. Whatever your needs are, and wherever you are in the country, there's something here that will fulfil your every need.

Whether you're a trucker, a salesman, a family, or simply someone who drives a lot (like me!) this book will be invaluable. I'm not saying it should replace your AA handbook, but I'm sure there's room in your glove box for both.....

The AA gave me a great break all those years ago - now let them give you a break! Thank you, Automobile Association!

Sally B

Sick of getting the same over-priced food in identikit motorway service stations? So were Bill Dickenson and Carol Mackaoui, until they started venturing into the roadside cafés and truckstops that can be found all over Britain. And, once they'd started, there was no stopping them. Having already converted all their friends and families they've now put together this guide to help the average road user make that break too. Roadside Cafés and Truckstops offers a comprehensive listing of roadside cafés and truckstops around the country, with photos, location maps and a list of the services they offer in addition to food.

The average roadside café or truckstop may not look as smart on the outside as some of the motorway service stations, but once you get over the threshold they're a revelation. Every one has its own individual character and ambience. Without exception they're clean and friendly and offer great value for money. They serve good, home-cooked food at sensible prices. They're all worth a try.

If you're a little wary of straying off the beaten path, take heart. These are not intimidating places full of hard-living hauliers! Every roadside café and truckstop in this book has been visited, interviewed, photographed and assessed. Many of the team who helped put this book together are women who went in to every establishment they visited on their own and in every case were given a warm welcome – long before anyone discovered they were researching this book.

So, if you've not tried a roadside café or truckstop before hopefully this book will inspire you to give one a go. If you're already a convert, then enjoy discovering places you may not have found before.

How to use the Guide

Penrith Truckstop

Haweswater Road, Penrith Industrial Estate, Penrith CA11 9EH
Tel: 01768 866 995

Directions: Exit the M6 at Junction 40 and follow the signs into Penrith. At the intersection with the A66 follow signs to the town centre. At the mini roundabout, go left and follow the signs to the truckstop – along the road on the left opposite BOCM.

It's well worth a five-minute detour off the motorway to find this well-run truckstop owned by Alan Jenkinson, where the staff are cheery and friendly and the overall atmosphere really welcoming.
There's plenty of car parking around the building plus well-maintained gardens that the customers appreciate.
The restaurant seats 100 and is very practical. All-day breakfast menus start at £3.20 through to £5.60 while other meals in the £5.00 range might include mince and dumpling or chicken and leek pie, all served with vegetables and potatoes and good value for money.
Upstairs is pleasant, modernized lounge with leather chairs, TV and a small stage, bar and dance floor. This connects with another room that is used for seminars and meetings.

OPENING TIMES
Mon-Sat: 06.00 - 13.30
Sun: 12.00 - 21.30
Public holidays: Closed

FACILITIES
Disabled facilities
Washroom for drivers
Newspapers, Cash machine
Parking: cars/trucks: plenty
Security: CCTV/fenced area for trucks
Caravans/coaches welcome

ACCOMMODATION
1 Single room (£20)
Secure entry

FOOD AND DRINK
Seating: 100
Daily specials, Kids' menu
Vegetarian menu
Alcoholic beverages in bar

No credit cards

The directory is arranged in four regions, and in alphabetical location order within each region. Each region has an introductory page with a map and list of the counties included in that region. The regions are colour coded; Green: South Wales and the West Country, Orange: Central and Eastern England, Red: North Wales, the Midlands and the North, Blue: Northern England Scotland. The county map on page 8 shows the regions.

Address and contact details are provided for each establishment.

Directions are included for each entry

Description – this is taken from the inspector's report and includes price information, as well as an indication of the style of the establishment.

Prices of example dishes have been provided by the establishments but should be taken as a guide only, as prices can change at any time.

Opening times are provided.

Facilities information includes whether there are facilities for disabled customers; if newspapers are provided; if there is a 'Cash Back' facility and/or an ATM; if there is a washroom for drivers. This section also includes information about parking – whether there is parking for trucks (including refrigeration units); if you can park overnight and whether this is charged; car park security (CCTV etc.); if caravans, motor vans and coaches are welcome, whether there is a shop on site, and so on.

Accommodation – some establishments have bedrooms. We indicate the number of rooms and whether they are single, double or family rooms; whether they have en suite facilities; and the price. Please be aware that bedrooms have not been inspected, and details are included for your information only.

Food & Drink – this section includes number of seats; outdoor eating; children's and vegetarian menus; and if alcohol is served. We also indicate where credit cards are not accepted.

Maps - Each entry includes a map with the establishment located on it.

Inspections – every establishment in the guide has been visited by MC Handbooks Ltd. Please bear in mind, however, that places may change hands at any time. Please let us know if you visit any roadside cafes or truckstops which are not included in the guide but which you would like to recommend. Please write to The Editor, AA Lifestyle Guides, Fanum House, Basing View, Basingstoke, RG21 4EA.

POND STREET
ELMDON
LITTLEBURY
SAFFRON WALDEN
LANGLEY VILLAGE FETE
AUGUST
BANK HOLIDAY MONDAY
1p.m. START

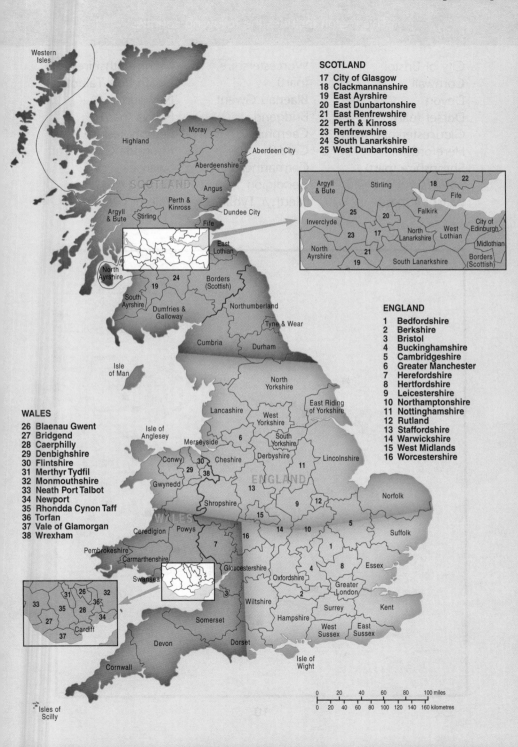

County Map

SCOTLAND
17 City of Glasgow
18 Clackmannanshire
19 East Ayrshire
20 East Dunbartonshire
21 East Renfrewshire
22 Perth & Kinross
23 Renfrewshire
24 South Lanarkshire
25 West Dunbartonshire

ENGLAND
1 Bedfordshire
2 Berkshire
3 Bristol
4 Buckinghamshire
5 Cambridgeshire
6 Greater Manchester
7 Herefordshire
8 Hertfordshire
9 Leicestershire
10 Northamptonshire
11 Nottinghamshire
12 Rutland
13 Staffordshire
14 Warwickshire
15 West Midlands
16 Worcestershire

WALES
26 Blaenau Gwent
27 Bridgend
28 Caerphilly
29 Denbighshire
30 Flintshire
31 Merthyr Tydfil
32 Monmouthshire
33 Neath Port Talbot
34 Newport
35 Rhondda Cynon Taff
36 Torfan
37 Vale of Glamorgan
38 Wrexham

South Wales and the West Country

This region includes the following counties:

City of Bristol
Cornwall
Devon
Dorset (part)
Gloucestershire (part)
Herefordshire
Shropshire (part)
Somerset
Wiltshire (part)

Worcestershire (part)
Blaenau Gwent
Bridgend
Caerphilly
Cardiff
Carmarthenshire
Ceridigion
Merthyr Tydfil

Monmouthshire
Neath Port Talbot
Newport
Powys (part)
Pembrokeshire
Rhondda Cynon Taff
Swansea
Torfaen
Vale of Glamorgan

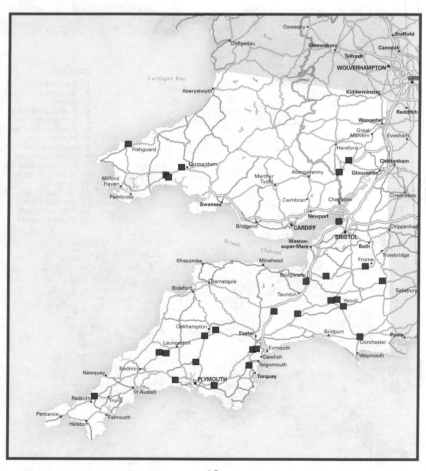

Albion Inn & Truckstop

14 Bath Road, Ashcott, Bridgwater TA7 9QT
Tel: 01458 210281

Directions: From M5 Junction 23 take the A39 towards Glastonbury. You'll find the Albion Inn on the right hand side of the road just after you come into the speed limit for Ashcott. The car park is the right turn just after the main building – it's large but slightly uneven.

The Albion is run by Peter and Glynis who, since taking over in August 2004, are on a mission to put it back on the map. Peter is a former lorry driver who has run a café in Exmouth but wants to do his bit to keep truckstops going. So far so good. The building may look austere but inside there's a friendly welcoming atmosphere.

An extensive menu covers both breakfast and dinner: portions are generous and prices reasonable. Breakfasts cover the usual range of full English, with vegetarian options. The dinner menu ranges from sausages and burgers through to soup and ploughmans and on to a massive mixed grill that includes rump steak, gammon, lamb chop, kidney, liver and sausage! Most dishes come with chips as standard, but you can have boiled or mashed potatoes as well as green veg. There's also a full selection of desserts.

Agents for CDC truck accessories.

OPENING TIMES

Mon-Thu:	07.00 - 20.00
Fri-Sat:	07.00 - 15.00
Sun;	
Public Holidays:	10.00 - 15.00

FACILITIES

Disabled facilities (2005)
Washroom for drivers 24hrs
Newspapers: read only
Parking: cars: plenty; trucks 20–26, refrigeration units off 22.00.
Security: floodlit overnight
Caravans/motor homes/coaches welcome

ACCOMMODATION

None – some in pub nearby

FOOD AND DRINK

Seating: 24
Daily specials; Kids' menu
Vegetarian menu
Alcoholic beverages
No credit cards

Anthea's Country Kitchen

A30, Plusha Altarnum, Launceston PL15 7RR
Tel: 01566 782014

Directions: On A30 west, Anthea's is a mile further on from the turning to Lewannick and Polyphant. Eastbound, look for a sliproad to the right after Trewint and Fivelanes.

Until five years ago, the building was part of a filling station adjacent, but Anthea MacDonald opened it up independently as a café and truckstop for truckers and holidaymakers, as well as locals in the winter.

Though only five years old, the café has an old-fashioned feel to it, with iron-based tables and two oak dressers as well as a stuffed fox in a glass case.

Anthea's specials include roasts with vegetables and jacket potato at £4.75; cottage pie, or liver and bacon at £4.25. Desserts are all priced at £2.25, among them, syrup or jam sponge or apple crumble.

Perhaps the most remarkable feature of Anthea's Country Kitchen is the incredible collection of over 450 teapots, lined up on shelves around the walls of the café. No two are the same.

OPENING TIMES
Mon-Fri: 06.00 - 20.00
Sat: 06.00 - 19.00
Sun;
Public holidays: 07.00 - 18.00

FACILITIES
Washroom for drivers
Parking: cars: 50; trucks: 30, parking £10 a night including meal
Security: lit overnight
Caravans/coaches: no

FOOD AND DRINK
Seating: 50
Outdoor eating area
Daily specials
Kids' menu
Vegetarian menu
No alcoholic beverages

No credit cards

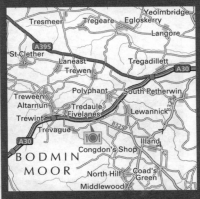

Avon Lodge

Third Way, Avonmouth BS11 9YP
Tel: 0117 982 7706 Fax: 0117 982 1081

Directions: Take M5 Junction 18, following signs to Avonmouth & Docks. At first roundabout turn right into Avonmouth Trading Estate. Drive down the road and turn left just past 'The Raceway'. Follow road round and Avon Lodge is on the left. Car park entrance is just beyond the building and parking is at rear of building.

As you drive through Avonmouth Trading Estate on your way to Paul Bawn's Avon Lodge you may wonder where on earth you're going, but the food when you get there makes the trip worthwhile. To find the parking area you need to drive up the right hand side of the building and it then becomes clear how to reach the parking behind the building.

As you walk through the front entrance of the building you will find a kiosk selling refreshments. A lounge for drivers is straight ahead of you.

The canteen is along the corridor to the left and you walk into a brightly lit room with smart formica tables. A typical special is beef and mushroom cobblers with peas, veg of the day, cream potatoes and tea or coffee. All for just £4.40. There are plenty of other choices – a full breakfast for £2.85, omelettes, sandwiches, cakes and desserts.

OPENING TIMES
Mon: 07.00 - 23.00
Tue-Fri: 06.30 - 23.30
Sat: 06.30 - 11.30
Sun;
Public Holidays: Closed

FACILITIES
Disabled facilities
Washroom for drivers
Newspapers
Parking: cars: 50; trucks: 60.
Security: floodlit
Caravans/coaches welcome

ACCOMMODATION
8 Doubles: £12 (p.p)

FOOD AND DRINK
Seating: 90
Daily specials
Alcoholic beverages

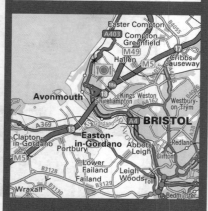

The Captain's Table

Goodwick, Fishguard Harbour, Fishguard, Pembrokeshire SA64 9EQ

Tel: 01348 873814

Directions: Take the A40 or A487 to Fishguard. Follow directions to harbour. Captain's Table café is part of the Texaco service station.

On the beautiful north coast of Pembrokeshire, as you approach Fishguard harbour and ferry service, is a Texaco service station, part of which houses the Captain's Table Café. Do not be put off by the plain exterior. Once inside, you will appreciate the charm of an old-fashioned seaside café, with the red brick walls and tables covered with red and white gingham tablecloths.

The menu offers breakfasts at £4.00; a variety of sandwiches, plain or toasted from between £1.80 and £2.75 and jacket potatoes from £2.30. The children's menu starts at £1.50, and includes a glass of squash. There are also daily specials.

Upstairs is the Bosun's Locker, a licensed function room, used mostly for private events. There is also a patio conservatory.

Owned by Mr Wentworth, the café has accommodation available on the first floor with 17 double bedrooms at £35.00 a night, breakfast included.

OPENING TIMES
Mon-Sun:
Public Holidays: 09.00 - 15.00

FACILITIES
Disabled facilities
Newspapers
Cash machine nearby
Parking: cars/trucks: plenty
Caravans/coaches welcome

ACCOMMODATION
17 Doubles: £35.00

FOOD AND DRINK
Seating: 80
Daily specials
Kids' menu
Vegetarian menu
No alcoholic beverages

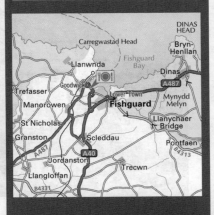

Cartgate Picnic Site

A303, Stoke-sub-Hamdon TA14 6RA
Tel: 07815 667536

Directions: Off the A303/A3088 roundabout, seven miles east of Ilminster. Look for 'Picnic Site' signs.

The site is owned and operated by the South Somerset District Council, but the Diner is operated by an independent trader under licence.

The 'Diner on the Cartgate Picnic Site' is in a landscaped area, with trees and shrubs planted in the grassed areas around the various parking areas. There are picnic tables, public toilets and a tourist information centre on the site.

There is a separate parking area for trucks, with no overnight charge. If the drivers have a meal in the café there is a shower available for £1.50.

The spotlessly clean Diner serves the usual food that one would expect including specials like roast beef or pork or chicken served with vegetables; steak and mushroom pie, and desserts like apple pie or apple and blackberry pie.

The picnic site is close to tourist attractions like Montacute House; The Haynes Motor Museum at Sparkford, and Yeovilton naval aircraft museum.

OPENING TIMES
Mon-Sun: 24 hours

FACILITIES
Disabled facilities
Washroom for drivers: £1.50 for HGV drivers who eat
Newspapers: read only
Parking: cars: 100; trucks: 60
Security: lighting
Caravans/coaches welcome
Garden
Children's play area

FOOD AND DRINK
Seating: 40
Outdoor eating area
Daily specials
Kids' menu
Vegetarian menu
No alcoholic beverages

No credit cards

The Cottage Café

Tenby Road, Llanddowror SA33 4HJ

Directions: A477 south of St Clears en route to Tenby in the village of Llanddowror. The café is on the left-hand side, with adjacent parking.

On entering the village of Llanddowror you'll see a pretty pink-painted house that is the Cottage Café, with plenty of parking.
Inside, the café has pale yellow painted walls and pine panelling with blue banquettes around the tables. On the walls are photographs of local point-to-point events, reflecting owner Michael Spuffard's interest in horses. There are also framed photogaraphs of various trucks and lorries.
The café is small and pleasant with a welcoming atmosphere. The present owners only took over in September 2004, but their reputation for good food is spreading and they are very happy with how their business is growing.
All-day full Pembrokeshire breakfasts are £3.00. Other dishes to choose from might be battered cod, chips and peas for £4.50 or vegetarian lasagne with cream cheese at £5.25. Children's menus and puddings start from £1.50 and are part of an interesting menu, which also includes local Welsh dishes.

OPENING TIMES
Mon-Fri:	07.00 - 14.30
Sat:	07.30 - 14.00
Sun;	
Public holidays:	Closed

FACILITIES
Disabled facilities
Newspapers
Parking: cars/trucks: plenty
Caravans/coaches welcome

FOOD AND DRINK
Seating: 40
Daily specials
Kids' menu
Vegetarian menu
No alcoholic beverages

No credit cards

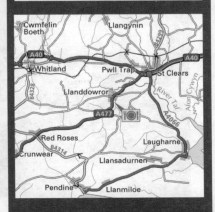

First Motorway Services

A40 Northbound, Symonds Yat Services, Whitchurch, Ross-on-Wye HR9 6DP
Tel: 01633 881551

Directions: Near Whitchurch, west of Ross-on-Wye, on northbound side of A40 and within BP service station area. Can be accessed from both directions.

A new, independently run restaurant (owned by Rob Millar) with excellent facilities for all travellers and truckers, it has won a 'Coach Stop' award and complimentary reports of the restaurant have been received from an Egon Ronay food critic.

The reception area has a well-stocked store selling drinks, sweets, newpapers and model transport vehicles.

There are two serving counters, one for hot foods. Breakfast can be purchased either by item, with individual packets of cereals, croissants, etc., or from the buffet, where the big hot cooked breakfasts are offered at £6.99, which includes coffee and tea. There is a substantial menu of other delicious foods as well as an interesting menu for children.

For £3.88 you can buy a thermos filled with a hot drink of your choice to take away with you.

Toilets are excellent and have won a national award for 'Loo of the Year'.

There is a small in-house entertainment area and fruit machines.

OPENING TIMES
Mon-Sun: 24 hours

FACILITIES
Disabled facilities
Newspapers
Cash machine
Parking: cars/trucks: plenty
Caravans/coaches welcome
Garden

FOOD AND DRINK
Seating: 100
Outdoor eating area
Daily specials
Kids' menu
Vegetarian menu
No alcoholic beverages

The French Hen

Ross Park, Ross-on-Wye HR9 7QJ
Tel: 01989 769000

Directions: On the A449 dual carriageway, just off Junction 4 of M50 at Ross-on-Wye. The French Hen, with the distinctive French Hen logo, can be found next to the Ross Labels factory outlet.

Owned by Delice de France, this café is modern and very stylishly furnished. It has a few outdoor tables and chairs for diners wanting to eat their meals in the fresh air. On the menu, together with a selection of hot savoury dishes, there are fresh filled rustic rolls and baguettes, with prices ranging from £2.35 to £3.25. Grilled panninis with lots of interesting fillings like chargrilled vegetables, start at £3.50. All-day breakfasts are also on offer – you can order them with a choice of five items. The price, including tea or coffee is £3.95. Takeaways are also available.

In the restaurant, you'll find an attractive counter and basket display of local items for sale: apple juice; jams; chutneys; cheeses; pâtés and chocolates, to name just a few. The café has a large paved forecourt that provides plenty of off-road parking.

OPENING TIMES
Mon-Sat: 08.00 - 18.00
Sun: 10.00 - 17.00
Public holidays: 08.00 - 18.00

FACILITIES
Disabled facilities
Newspapers
Parking: cars/trucks: plenty
Caravans/coaches welcome

FOOD AND DRINK
Seating: 50
Daily specials
Kids' menu
Vegetarian menu
No alcoholic beverages

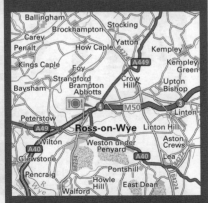

Graham's Cafe

Taunton Road, North Pellerton, Devon TA6 6PR
Tel: 07815 667536

Directions: M5 Junction 24. Follow signs from motorway to the services. At roundabout turn left, following sign to 'local services'. Graham's is just up the road on the left hand side. Just before you get there is a 'Heavy Vehicles Turning' sign. There's also a petrol station that charges for overnight parking.

Graham's Café was opened 16 years ago by Simon Rivers who had been a driver for as many years again. He seems to have got the recipe right.

The interior is a mix of cheerful blues and terracotta, with plants in the windows. The menus are all up on boards around the counter and there's plenty of choice: T-bone steak, chips peas and onions are £5.75; sausage, egg and chips with a bottle of water cost just £3.55, with speedy service and the food arriving piping hot – all good value. There are also plenty of salad options available and deserts.

One side of the room is a no-smoking area. High chairs for babies are available on request. In one corner there's a TV with the volume kept at a reasonable level and there are daily papers for customers to read during their stopover.

OPENING TIMES
Mon:	07.00 - 20.00
Tue-Thu:	06.30 - 20.00
Sat:	07.00 - 23.00
Sun;	
Public holidays:	07.00 - 23.00

FACILITIES
Washroom and showers for drivers
Newspapers: read only
Parking: cars/trucks: plenty
Caravans welcome
Coaches: 2 days' notice required

FOOD AND DRINK
Seating: 40
Outdoor eating area
Daily specials; Kids' menu
Vegetarian menu
No alcoholic beverages

No credit cards

Greasy Joe's Café

Lorry Park, Old Swindon Road, Cirencester GL7 1NP
Tel: 01285 640275

Directions: Enter Cirencester on the the A417/419. At roundabout follow sign to the lorry park and superstore. Greasy Joe's is located in the lorry park and is well signed.

Easy to locate, this great café is a joy to visit. The owners, brothers Mark and Lloyd, have been there for about 27 years and established a character of their own. Inside the café are glass cabinets displaying mobiles, and collectables for sale, and walls have notices of items for sale, vacancies and so on – that make amusing reading while you enjoy the large portions that are prepared in the open kitchen at the rear of the café. A fruit machine and retro gobstopper sweet dispenser are also part of the decoration.

The café is quite intimate, seating 38. Breakfasts are either big, or vegetarian, at £4.75 or small at £3.75 or you can try omelettes; soup and roll £1.20 or go for a full meal of chilli or curry at £4.95 or faggots or lamb chop with chips or mashed potatoes, peas and gravy, starting at £4.75.

OPENING TIMES
Mon-Fri: 06.00 - 18.00
Sat-Sun;
Public holidays: 06.00 - 17.00

FACILITIES
Disabled facilities
Washroom for drivers
Newspapers
Parking: cars/trucks: plenty
Caravans/coaches welcome

FOOD AND DRINK
Seating: 38
Outside eating area
Daily specials
Kids' menu
Vegetarian menu
No alcoholic beverages

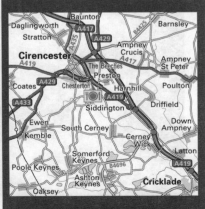

The Gorge Café

Glovers Walk, Yeovil BA20 1LH

Tel: 01935 422370

Directions: On entering Yeovil, follow the signs to the Town Centre and then to Quedam car parking and the bus station. The Gorge Café is in Glovers Walk Centre.

Established for over 20 years, the café has a special atmosphere of its own. The customers are either waiting for buses, meeting visitors or enjoying the delights of Yeovil. It's a busy café that inside has an intimate atmosphere and slightly resembles a Swiss chalet, with wooden seating in booths, red banquette seating surrounded by bowls of plastic flowers, baskets of hanging flowers hung on the dark red concrete posts, plus lots of low-slung lanterns. The friendly staff start serving at 07.00 in the weekdays. Breakfasts are a memorable feast with the special at £6.60. There is a full menu of regular meals, omelettes with various fillings, quiches, and sausage dishes starting at £3.15. Waffles, cakes and ice creams are also popular.

OPENING TIMES

Mon-Sat: 07.00 - 17.30
Sun;
Public holidays: 09.00 - 14.30

FACILITIES

Disabled facilities
Parking: cars: plenty; trucks: a few nearby
Caravans: no
Coaches welcome

FOOD AND DRINK

Seating: 49
Daily specials
Kids' menu
Vegetarian menu
No alcoholic beverages

No credit cards

The Haldon Grill Café

A380, Telegraph Hill, Kennford, Exeter EX6 7XW

Tel: 01392 833700

Directions: Turn off the A38 south onto the A380. The café is about half a mile on the left. A flyover is being constructed which will ease access for northbound traffic.

The Haldon Grill Café is at the top of a steep incline known as Telegraph Hill. It is in front of two buildings that were once a garage and a café.

In the past, cars and lorries would overheat climbing the hill (it has now been improved), so drivers would wait at the top of the hill and have refreshments while their vehicles cooled down.

The view looking out over the River Exe is, according to the writer Ray Cattell, the 'most delightful scene in Devon'.

The grill-on-the-hill, as owners Andrew and Lisa Harvey call it, serves locals and passers by, providing all-day breakfast at £3.20; gammon, egg and chips £4.20; plaice and chips £3.95. There are no daily specials, but the grill will cook anything to order. Desserts include spotted dick and chocolate sponge with various fillings.

OPENING TIMES

Mon-Fri:	07.00 - 16.00
Sat:	07.00 - 15.00
Sun:	09.00 - 14.00
Public holidays:	Closed

FACILITIES

Disabled facilities
Parking: cars: 40; trucks: 10
Caravans/coaches welcome
Garden

FOOD AND DRINK

Seating: 50
Outdoor eating area
Daily specials
Kids' menu
Vegetarian menu
No alcoholic beverages

No credit cards

Ibis Roadhouse Diner

Harcombe Cross Garage, Harcombe, Chindleigh TQ13 0DF
Tel: 01626 854555

Directions: After Exeter take A38 dual carriageway west and two miles after Exeter racecourse, Ibis Roadhouse is on BP/Spar site. It can be reached eastwards by taking a slip road off near Harcombe and going under the A38.

By the side of the BP/Spar service station is a bright blue extended Portakabin. Opened in 2004, this diner looks very inviting with yellow doors and windows, terraced decking with tables and chairs, umbrellas and baskets of flowers. Managed by Rose, the Roadhouse is a happy place that has become very popular. Cheerful staff wear chefs' bright harlequin trousers, a theme continued throughout the interior of the cabin where tables are high and matched with corresponding stools and window benches.

A large menu ranges from English breakfasts to baguettes and pizzas and on to more serious options including local lamb, and Somerset pork or chicken, served with potatoes and vegetables at £7.25. Vegetarians are offered a fresh vegetable roast, and there are traditional meals like mixed grill or gammon steak starting at £4.50. Takeaway meals are also available.

OPENING TIMES
Mon-Sat: 07.00 - 21.00
Sun;
Public Holidays: 07.00 - 15.00

FACILITIES
Disabled facilities
Newspapers
Cash machine in garage
Parking: cars/trucks: plenty
Caravans/coaches welcome

FOOD AND DRINK
Seating: 42
Outdoor seating area
Daily specials
Kids' menu
Vegetarian menu
No alcoholic beverages

No credit cards accepted

Jolly Diner

Townsend Garage, Tintinhull, Yeovil BA22 8PF
Tel: 01935 822636

Directions: Off the eastbound A303 from Yeovil, between the A3088 and the A37 roundabouts. Set behind a Shell petrol station and Townsend garage.

This unusual café is especially interesting for car enthusiasts. While enjoying a cup of coffee you can feast your eyes on the white stretch limos and the two beautiful and immaculate vintage Rolls Royces from the 1930s (available for hire). There is also a red 1950s MG convertible.

Mrs Taylor, the owner, runs the restaurant as a licensed fast food outlet. However, the staff are very helpful and are generally happy to try and prepare a particular request if it is not on the menu.

English breakfasts are popular, but you can also buy hot and cold meals with vegetables and chips, burgers, and puddings. It's a pity to rush straight to the fast food route, as the café is pleasantly decorated, with flowers on all the tables.

OPENING TIMES
Mon-Sat: 09.00 - 17.00
Sun: 08.00 - 17.00

FACILITIES
Newspapers
Parking: cars/trucks: plenty
Caravans/coaches welcome
Garden

FOOD AND DRINK
Seating: 100
Outdoor eating area
Daily specials
Kids' menu
Vegetarian menu
Alcoholic beverages

M & M Snack Bar

A386 (A30) Picnic Area, Sourton Cross EX20 1LX
Tel: 01837 55436

Directions: Leave the A30 at its junction with the A386 and head north. Café and truck park are on the right hand side.

The Snack Bar owned by Mitchel and Mowlem is a Portakabin-type of building on a council-owned truck/car park, and is used by lorry drivers who park there for the night. Parking is free, and the area is lit. A truck driver did say that in winter it can be pretty uncomfortable in a high wind, as when it blows across this exposed area it can rock the vehicles to an alarming degree!

The site is on the edge of Dartmoor, and there are spectacular views from this high point. Okehampton, with its many attractions, is nearby and Castle Drogo, the Finch Foundry and the spectacular Lydford Gorge are all close by on Dartmoor.

The café does not offer 'special' meals but everything is prepared on site.

OPENING TIMES
Mon-Fri: 07.00 - 21.00
Sat: 07.00 - 16.00
Sun: 09.00 - 18.00
Public Holidays: 09.00 - 19.00

FACILITIES
Newspapers: read only
Parking: cars: 25; trucks: 30
Caravans/coaches welcome
Security: lit overnight

FOOD AND DRINK
Seating: 25
Outdoor eating area
Kids' menu
Vegetarian menu
No alcoholic beverages

No credit cards

Newcott Chef

A303, Yarcombe, Honiton EX14 9ND
Tel: 01404 861277

Directions: On the A303, midway between Honiton and Ilminster, on the south side of the road.

The Newcott Chef overlooks the beautiful Blackdown Hills and is privately owned by D Lavey. The café has a comfortable, well-used appearance, and inside, are plants, a fish tank and a pool table. There's a bar at the rear and a separate no-smoking area. Fifteen years ago dinner dances were held here with invited hosts including Steve Wright, Dave Lee Travis, Eric Bruton and the Wurzells making appearances. Jimmy Saville is an occasional customer, who orders gammon, egg and chips. The menu is traditional and prices are only slightly more than those at dedicated truckstops. Standard breakfast is £4.70; big breakfast £5.70; burger and chips £4.30. Desserts include pancakes at £2.80. Pot of tea (2 cups) £1.30.

There are plenty of visitor attractions in the area including Escot Historic Gardens at Ottery-St-Mary with its otters and red squirrels; Forde Abbey at Chard and Longleat at Warminster.

OPENING TIMES

Mon-Thu:	07.00 - 18.00
Fri:	07.00 - 19.00
Sat:	07.00 - 18.00
Sun:	07.00 - 19.00

FACILITIES

Disabled facilities
Newspapers
Parking: cars: 30; trucks: 5
Caravans/coaches welcome

FOOD AND DRINK

Seating: 100
Kids' menu
Vegetarian menu
Alcoholic beverages

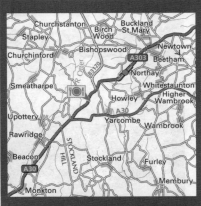

Nunney Catch Café

Nunney Roundabout, Nr Frome BA11 4NZ
Tel: 01373 836331

Directions: On A361 Shepton Mallet to Frome road. Nunney Catch Café is set back from the roundabout at the junction with A359.

Due to its location and atmosphere, the café, run by Jackie Callow for the last 18 years, continues to be a popular stopping place. The comprehensive menu is altered daily, the food is good and there's a licensed bar so you can enjoy a drink with your meal.

Interior decoration is based on trucks, truckers and vehicles, and the originality of the servery, which is designed and decorated to resemble a flat-bed truck, says much about the café. The walls are festooned with fantastic memorabilia, including mugs brought in by customers from all corners of the world. Behind the café you will find a small, enclosed water garden and rockery, an ideal quiet place to sit after a long day on the road. Because the café has a large parking space and is often empty of trucks at the weekends, it is a popular and regular meeting place for motorcyclists .

OPENING TIMES
Mon-Fri:	07.00 - 19.30
Fri:	07.00 - 16.30
Sat:	07.30 - 13.30
Sun:	Closed

FACILITIES
Disabled facilities
Washroom for drivers
Newspapers
Cash machine
Parking: cars/trucks: plenty
Security: CCTV 24 hours
Caravans/coaches welcome
Garden

FOOD AND DRINK
Seating: 60
Outdoor eating area
Daily specials
Kids' menu
Vegetarian menu
Alcoholic beverages

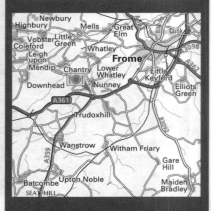

Old Mill Café

A477, Llanddowror SA33 4HR
Tel: 01994 230836 Mob: 07985 346730

Directions: On A477 after village of Llanddowror, en route to Tenby, set back on right side with big truck parking area, well signed.

Roxanne Tracey, a trained lawyer, has returned to her roots in this pretty area of Wales to run the Old Mill café. A restaurant and bar are in course of completion in the adjacent old stone barn building.

The buildings are in a very beautiful Welsh country environment and the big garden is lush with grass, trees, bushes and a mass of wild flowers.

The café is currently concentrating on the all-day breakfasts and Sunday roasts at £4.50, with some other local foods on as well. Seating 25, the café is pleasantly comfortable, with a very friendly atmosphere.

The bar, with beams, stone floor and local stone walls is an intimate room with comfortable chairs. It leads through to the restaurant, which is a 16th-century converted woollen mill that promises to be an exciting looking baronial hall for the planned restaurant.

OPENING TIMES
Mon-Sun:
Public holidays: 07.30 - 16.00
(summer 17.00)

FACILITIES
Newspapers
Parking: cars/trucks: plenty
Caravans/coaches welcome
Garden
Children's play area

FOOD AND DRINK
Seating: 25
Outdoor eating area
Daily specials
Kids' menu
Vegetarian menu
Alcoholic beverages

No credit cards

RJ's Café

The Aller Layby, Torquay Road, Kingskerswell, Torquay, Devon TQ12 5AT
Tel: 01386 881521

Directions: Heading for Torquay from Newton Abbott on A380, start looking for a café sign on the left in the trees. The café is in a 'pull-off' area and cannot immediately be seen.

Now sited on what was the old Torbay road is RJ's Café, or as it used to be called, Romany Jones' Café was originally an old-fashioned fairground wagon built by the firm Orton & Spooner in about 1890. It would have been pulled on its iron wheels by six shire horses or two elephants and possibly, later by a steam engine. In the 1900s it became a café and restroom for travellers and continues to be so. Now owned by Peter Smallwood, the café provides a variety of meals, including chilli con carne, curry or steak and kidney pie all served at £3.95, or steak and chips at £4.95. There is a range of desserts including spotted dick, toffee sponge, apple crumble, all priced at £1.95. A cup of tea is 60p.

There are pleasant walks created by a local landowner in the woods behind the trailer.

OPENING TIMES

Mon-Fri:	07.30 - 14.30
Sat:	06.00 - 13.30
Public holidays:	13.30 - 17.30
Sun:	Closed

FACILITIES

Newspapers: read only
Parking: cars: 20 along slip road; trucks: 10 along slip road
Caravans welcome
Coaches: no
Garden

FOOD AND DRINK

Seating: 60
Outdoor eating area
Daily specials
Vegetarian menu
No alcoholic beverages

No credit cards

Route 46

Directions: From M5 take Junction 9 onto the A46 at Evesham. Route 46 is after the roundabout, heading towards the village of Beckford. It is well signposted on the right-hand side within a Shell service station.

A spacious, recently refurbished café, modern and minimalist, with large glass windows making it light and airy. Such is the success of this café, you need to book a table if you want to eat there at weekends and public holidays. The team here under Dawn Wall's management, provides a wonderful welcome, clearly great enthusiasm is being invested into this café. The bar area is very comfortable with stylish leather chairs, and opens onto a patio – the perfect place for summer eating and drinking. The bar is fully licensed and open normal hours.

As well as the all-day breakfast at £4.95, the comprehensive menu offers daily specials: a 16oz (453g) gammon steak or rump steaks; hot or cold roasts with vegetables or salads starting at £6.95, with puddings at £3.95 and baguettes and omelettes as well. A 'Route 46' double platter is £3.95.

OPENING TIMES

Mon-Fri:	06.00 - 21.00
Sat:	07.00 - 17.00
Sun:	08.00 - 17.00

FACILITIES

Disabled facilities
Washroom for drivers
Newspapers
Cash machine in garage
Parking: cars: plenty
trucks: plenty. Overnight
£7.50 inc. meal voucher
Caravans/coaches welcome

FOOD AND DRINK

Seating: 90
Daily specials
Kids' menu
Vegetarian menu
No alcoholic beverages

Silvey's

Draycot Cerne, Chippenham SN15 1AW
Tel: 01249 750645

Directions: M4 Junction 17. Signposted off the roundabout as 'lorry services'. Silvey's is on the right hand side of the road about two minutes down the B4122 as you drive away from the motorway junction. There's a board on the roadside to mark the entrance.

Like many truckstops, the outside of Silvey's is quite plain but inside is a different matter. Recently re-fitted, this truckstop sports a gleaming chrome counter and a smart separate kiosk area in the entrance for those wanting a quick stop for chocolates, drinks and magazines. The dining area has blue and white walls, wooden tables and country-style chairs and the food is great value – a tasty quiche and chips, a bottle of water and a newspaper came to just £3.50. Also on the day's menu are dishes like oriental chicken, as well as all the more traditional full breakfast options.

If you're just stopping to eat, parking is free and a shower costs £2. Overnight parking is either £9.00, which includes parking and a shower, or £12.00 that includes a £3.50 meal voucher.

There's a 24-hour automated diesel system for trucks using a fuel card with a pin number. IDS, AS 24, Silvey Card, Key Fuels, Fuelserve and UK Fuels are all accepted. Silvey's is managed by Tracey Hopson.

OPENING TIMES
Mon-Sat: 06.00 - 23.00
Sun;
Public holidays: Closed

FACILITIES
Disabled facilities
Washroom for drivers
Newspapers; Cash machine
Parking: cars: 20; trucks: 60
Security: CCTV/fenced
Caravans welcome
Coaches: advance notice required
Garden

FOOD AND DRINK
Seating: 40
Outdoor eating area
Daily specials
Kids' menu
Vegetarian menu
Alcoholic beverages

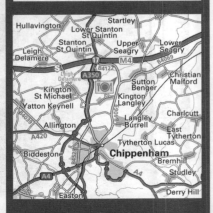

Smokey Joe's

Old A30, Blackwater, Scorrier, Cornwall TR14 5BJ
Tel: 01209 821810

Directions: From the south, follow the A30 dual carriageway to its end at a roundabout. Take the first road for Blackwater. Smokey Joe's is through the village on the right hand side. From the north, take the road to Blackwater at the A30/A390 roundabout.

Smokey Joe's has been a famous truckstop for over 60 years and has beautiful and haunting views over the western side of Cornwall towards the sea. There are many ruined tin-mining buildings to be seen and in the truckstop you can see a painting of a working tin mine.

Smokey's is typical of truckstops, nothing fussy. The menu here is varied and many locals eat here – to save cooking at home! Specials include roasts; steak pie, or chicken and bacon pie, all at £4.50 with a selection of homemade cakes and puddings from £2.00. A cup of tea is 60p. They have a 'Steak Night' once a month.

The Eden Project is probably the most famous attraction in the area – about 20 miles away. The beach is two miles away and Truro, with its lovely 19th-century Cathedral, is four miles away.

The owners are E. Walker and A Caddy.

Opening Times
Mon-Fri:	07.00 - 22.00
Sat:	08.00 - 20.00
Sun:	10.00 - 20.00
Public Holidays:	Closed

Facilities
Disabled facilities
Newspapers
Parking: cars: 30; trucks: 25: park only £4.00; park and main meal £8.50
Security: partly lit
Caravans/coaches welcome

Food and Drink
Seating: 60
Daily specials
Kids' menu
Vegetarian menu
Alcoholic beverages

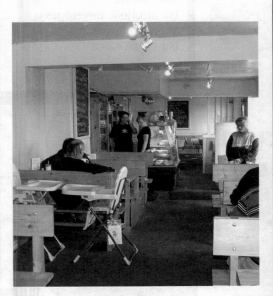

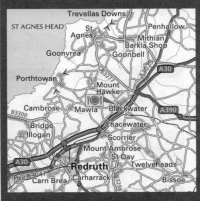

Tenby Road Service Station

Llsonnen Road, Carmarthen SA33 5DT
Tel: 01267 237854

Directions: On the A40, to the east of St Clears just before Carmarthen. The café shares a site with a Shell service station.

This roadside café sells fast food. It has a bar-style servery in the services shop, and there is also a separate seating area on the other side where customers can sit and enjoy a more leisurely break from their journey. The seating area is pleasantly decorated in pale yellow and light blue, and divided up by panels and planters. The children's corner has toys and building bricks and some small tables and chairs – a chance for some play time to break the journey.

The café, run by Mr Manning, is open from 07.00 to 14.30 Monday to Friday, and until 14.00 on Saturday. There's a choice of burgers, prices starting at £1.99; a selection of breakfasts at £2.25, or some light snacks such as egg and sausage rolls; sausage and onion rolls from £1.69, or baguettes with two fillings from £1.90.

OPENING TIMES
Mon-Fri:	07.00 - 14.30
Sat:	07.00 - 14.00
Sun;	
Public Holidays:	Closed

FACILITIES
Disabled facilities
Washroom for drivers
Newspapers
Cash machine
Parking: cars/trucks: plenty
Caravans/coaches welcome
Children's play area

FOOD AND DRINK
Seating: 80
Outside eating area
Kids' menu
No alcoholic beverages

No credit cards

Top of Town

A35, Top of the Town Car Park, Dorchester DT1 1XT
Tel: 01305 269199

Directions: Enter the town on A35, becoming B3150. The café is behind the Military Museum in the bus/coach park, set against the back wall on the left.

Mr Perritt's great little café is well known, and a popular meeting place for motorbike enthusiasts.

In summer, pots of flowers and a few tables are set outside the café. For anyone visiting the town or waiting for the bus, the café provides the perfect opportunity to relax with a mug of tea or coffee to accompany the full English breakfast. Also on the menu is a choice of hot and cold meals, as well as sweets, canned drinks and sandwiches to take away. The café has a good atmosphere, just the place to be on a cold day, with a mug of hot drink. Afternoon visitors can try the cakes, made by the local WI and sold along with ice cream for those warm sunny days.

Close to the Military Museum and the Tutankhamen exhibition, the café is just a short walk to this charming and historic military town.

OPENING TIMES

Mon-Fri:	06.30 - 19.00
Sat-Sun;	
Public holidays:	06.30 - 19.30

FACILITIES

Disabled facilities
Newspapers
Cash machine
Parking: cars/trucks: town car park
Caravans/coaches welcome
Children's play area

FOOD AND DRINK

Seating: 36
Outdoor eating area
Kids' menu
Vegetarian menu
No alcoholic beverages

No credit cards

Trewint Auto Services

A30, Trewint, Launceston PL15 7TF
Tel: 01566 880181

Directions: Twelve miles east of Bodmin on the A30. Café and filling station on the side of the road at Trewint. Look for the Texaco fuel sign.

The café is light and airy with two separate dining areas. The Trewint menu does not have a 'specials' board. A cup of tea with a biscuit is 69p. At the rear of the building there's a fully equipped bar with easy chairs, a pool table and gaming machines.

At the front of the café is a shop selling the usual necessities for motorists, and obviously, fuel is available at the pumps outside.

The establishment is owned by Mr Kumaraun, who also runs the bed and breakfast side of the business. There are no televisions in the bedrooms, but there are two in the public rooms downstairs.

There is plenty of parking space for truckers, with a charge of £9.99 that includes a main meal, hot drinks and showers and free flask fill.

OPENING TIMES

Mon-Fri:	06.00 - 22.00
Sat:	07.00 - 20.00
Sun:	07.00 - 18.00
Public holidays:	06.00 - 22.00

FACILITIES

Washroom for drivers
Newspapers
Parking: cars: 50; trucks: 30, parking £9.99 inc. main meal, hot drinks, showers and free flask filling.
Security: CCTV
Caravans/coaches welcome

ACCOMMODATION

3 Doubles: £24.99 (p.p.)
3 Singles: £24.99 (p.p.)

FOOD AND DRINK

Seating: 60
Outdoor eating area
Kids' menu; Vegetarian menu
Alcoholic beverages

Vines Close Farm

Dorchester Road, Henbury, Wimborne BH21 3RW
Tel: 01258 857278

Directions: Off the Wimborne Minster bypass, close to the intersection of A31 and A350.

This is much more than a café. Vines Close Farm is a country store, farm shop *and* café, easy to reach off the A31.

Well supported by locals, the café offers the most wonderful selection of homemade cakes, an interesting lunch menu with daily specials, including such delights as Somerset Brie salad, and speciality Dorset cream teas. The restaurant is very attractively decorated, having a cottage feel to it, and a welcoming atmosphere.

At the country store you can buy everything you need for the garden, from seeds to garden equipment, tools, beautiful garden planters and garden furniture. The farm shop sells local lamb, beef and pork as well as other enticing groceries, and once you have finished shopping you can relax in the tearoom.

Vines Close Farm has something for everyone. The owners have been so delighted by the success of their venture that they are planning to expand the existing facilities.

OPENING TIMES
Mon-Sat: 09.00 - 18.00
Sun: 10.00 - 12.30

FACILITIES
Disabled facilities
Washroom for drivers
Newspapers
Parking: cars: 30; trucks: 10
Caravans welcome
Coaches welcome: notice required

FOOD AND DRINK
Seating: 100
Outdoor eating area
Daily specials
Kids' menu
Vegetarian menu
No alcoholic beverages

The Westwood Café

Old A38, Lee Mill, Ivybridge, Devon PL21 9EF
Tel/Fax: 01752 894344

Directions: On the old A38 between Ivybridge and Plympton. Take the exit for Lee Mill and turn left at the intersection. Truckstop is behind the Jet filling station.

The café's substantial menu includes the usual all-day breakfast, midday meals and the day's specials, which might include steak and ale pie with potatoes and vegetables at £4.95, or sausage and mash with beans in onion gravy for £4.95. Desserts include apple pie, treacle pudding, jam roly-poly all served with custard or ice cream and priced at £2.25. There are also filled baguettes (hot or cold).

Behind the café there is a very pleasant walk along the banks of the river. A few miles a way, there's an active Abbey and a wildlife park.

There are two local public houses within walking distance for evenings after the café closes.

OPENING TIMES
Mon-Thu:	06.00 - 20.00
Fri:	06.00 - 17.00
Sat:	08.00 - 14.00
Sun; Public holidays:	Closed

FACILITIES
Disabled facilities
Washroom for drivers: free if parked, otherwise £1.00
Newspapers: read only
Parking: cars: 25; trucks: 36: £6.00
Caravans/coaches welcome

FOOD AND DRINK
Seating: 50
Daily specials
Kids' menu
Vegetarian menu
No alcoholic beverages

No credit cards

The Whitehouse Restaurant

A30 Exeter Road, Tongue End, Okehampton EX20 1QJ
Tel: 01837 840101

Directions: Heading west on the A30 between Exeter and Launceston, take the first turning signed for Okehampton. The café is signed from there. Accesible to westbound traffic only.

The Whitehouse, which was originally a truckstop, has been modernised and, along with the adjacent filling station, is owned and run by Mr and Mrs Snowden. It's in a great position high up on the edge of Dartmoor with south-facing views.

The usual breakfast is served plus specials: steak and kidney pie with chips and peas £5.70 or roast of the day, served with roast potatoes and vegetables £5.00. Homemade cheese, bacon and potato bake with vegetables £4.65. Fruit crumbles £2.60

The area round Okehampton has many places of interest worth visiting including Castle Drogo, designed by 20th-century architect Edwin Lutyens, or the beautiful Lydford Gorge that lies to the south on the edge of Dartmoor just off the A386.

OPENING TIMES
Mon-Sun:
Public holidays: 07.00 - 20.00

FACILITIES
Disabled facilities
Newspapers: in garage
Cash machine: in garage
Parking: cars: 40; trucks: 5
Caravans/coaches welcome
Garden
Children's play area

FOOD AND DRINK
Seating: 100
Outdoor eating area
Daily specials
Kids' menu
Vegetarian menu
No alcoholic beverages

The Willand Restaurant

Willand Service Station, Willand, Cullompton EX15 2PF
Tel: 01884 32282 Fax: 01884 33603

Directions: Exit the M5 at Junction 27. Head south on the B3181.
The café/filling station is through the village of Willand on the right.

The Willand Restaurant is at the southern edge of Willand village. The B3181 was once the main road from Taunton to Exeter, carrying heavy traffic that now uses the M5. The garage is a splendid example of 1930s garage construction, the upper level projecting over the fuel pumps to provide a waterproof canopy when filling up with petrol.

The restaurant, seating 80, is very smart. It is run by Sandra Goff, whose family has been operating from here for many years.

Meals available include roasts; steak and kidney pie; cottage pie; lasagne, all priced at £4.15. Puddings offered might be bread and butter pudding, apple pie or rice pudding for £2.75 each. Main meal and dessert for seniors is £4.15.

Adjacent to the restaurant is a Spar shop; a repair garage; an adventure playground for riding on diggers and tractors, and down the road is a farm with pick-your-own strawberries.

OPENING TIMES

Mon-Sun: 08.00 - 17.00
                    (later for parties)
Public holidays: Closed

FACILITIES

Disabled facilities
Newspapers
Parking: cars: 60; trucks: parking difficult
Caravans/coaches welcome
Garden

FOOD AND DRINK

Seating: 80
Daily specials
Kids' menu
Vegetarian menu
Alcoholic beverages

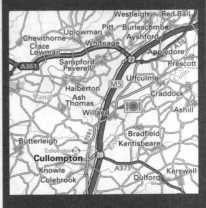

Windy Ridge Eating House

Trerulefoot, Saltash, Cornwall PL12 5BJ
Tel: 01752 851344 Fax 01752 851036
Email: windyridgediner@aol.com www.windyridgeeatinghouse.co.uk

Directions: On A38 between Liskeard and Saltash. At Trerulefoot, roundabout turn off south for Looe, Windy Ridge is 100 yards on the right.

Windy Ridge Eating House is a modern diner on the south of a hill overlooking the magnificent Devon countryside. The interior is smartly panelled in a pale wood with inset mirrors, giving a very spacious feel, while in the entrance you can photographs of the café as it was in the 1950s.

There is an extensive menu with a three-course meal costing £6.25, less £1.00 for pensioners. The price includes a cup of tea or coffee. Typical dishes are starters followed by steak and kidney pie and puddings such as ice cream or treacle sponge pudding. There are also specials on certain days like Mothers' Day and over the Christmas period.

Simon Bowden is the owner of this busy restaurant that serves regulars from the area and summer sun seekers. There is a small separate dining room (non-smoking) with full bar facilities. They accept function and party bookings.

Opening Times
Mon-Sat: 06.15 - 21.30 (Winter)
06.15 - 22.00 (Summer)
Sun: 08.00 - 21.30 (Winter)
07.30 - 22.00 (Summer)
Xmas & Boxing Day: Closed

Facilities
Disabled facilities
Washroom for drivers
Newspapers
Cash machine: in nearby garage
Parking: cars: 50; trucks: 20
Security: lit at night
Caravans/coaches welcome
Garden; Children's play area

Food and Drink
Seating: 60
Outdoor eating area
Daily specials; Kids' menu
Vegetarian menu
No alcoholic beverages

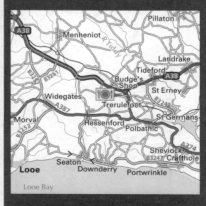

Central and Eastern England

This region includes the following counties:

Bedfordshire
Berkshire
Buckinghamshire
Cambridgeshire (part)
Dorset (part)
Essex
Gloucestershire (part)

Greater London
Hampshire
Isle of Wight
Hertfordshire
Kent
Northamptonshire
(part)

Norfolk (part)
Oxfordshire
Suffolk
East Sussex
West Sussex
Wiltshire (part)
Worcestershire (part)

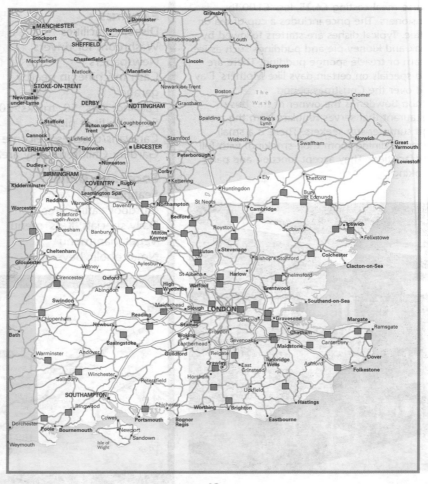

INDEX
Central and Eastern England

A20 Roadhouse

A20 Ashford Road, Lenham ME17 2DL
Tel: 01622 858555

Directions: The Roadhouse is about midway between Junctions 8 and 9 of the M20, on the A20 at Lenham.

Travellers have been eating at this café since the First World War. Photographs show the original café after it was bombed by the Germans.

Now called the A20 Roadhouse, the café has had many other names including Oasis, Rose of Trallee, Little Chest and The Singing Kettle. Specials include liver and bacon £2.80; chicken curry £3.20; rhubarb and custard £1.80. In addition, there is also a good selection of homemade cakes.

It is worth this detour onto the A20 for the drive along a good road to enjoy the Kent countryside. Two miles east of the Roadhouse is the pretty village of Charing, with its historic Bishop's Palace.

OPENING TIMES
Mon-Fri: 06.30 - 22.00
Sat: 07:00 - 13.00
Sun; Public holidays: Closed

FACILITIES
Newspapers
Parking: car: 20; trucks: 25
Security: CCTV
Caravans/coaches welcome

FOOD AND DRINK
Seating: 60
Daily specials
Kids' menu
Vegetarian menu
No alcoholic beverages

No credit cards

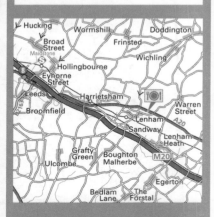

Abbotts Ann Café

Salisbury Road, Abbotts Ann, Andover SP11 7NX
Tel: 01264 710213
Directions: On the A343 between Andover and Salisbury.

A cheerful look has been give to this café which, with bright yellow exterior paintwork and a blue porch is easy to find. Owner Christine Forrester has recently re-launched this café, which now has a warm friendly atmosphere with plenty of laughter and great music.

Entering the café you will find large posters decorating the walls. An archway takes you into another light room that can be used for private parties or functions. In summer there are tables outside under a portico.

The café food is traditional but Christine uses local produce such as free-range eggs as much as possible. Another special is square sausages! Close to the Museum of Army Flying in Middle Wallop.

OPENING TIMES

Mon-Sat: 08.00 - 14.30
Sun;
Public holidays: 10.00 - 15.00

FACILITIES

Disabled facilities
Washroom for drivers
Newspapers
Parking: cars/trucks: plenty
Caravans welcome
Coaches: advance notice required

FOOD AND DRINK

Seating: 50
Outdoor eating area
Daily specials
Kids' menu
Vegetarian menu
No alcoholic beverages

No credit cards

Ace Café

Ace Corner, North Circular Road, Stonebridge NW10 7JD
Tel: 0208 961 1000 Fax: 0208 965 0160 Email: acecafe7@aol.com; www.ace-café-london.com

Directions: The Ace Café is on the original North Circular Road, now replaced by the new NCR (A406). Situated approximately half a mile from Hangar Lane roundabout (where A40 and A406 cross), drive east in the direction of Brent Cross. Take the first turn off left, which is elevated to traffic lights. Cross at the lights and the Ace Café is almost immediately on your left. Travelling east along the A406, consult the map or continue to the roundabout and return as above.

Relaunched in 1994 (in which The AA contributed motoring memorabilia and vintage vehicles) the Ace Café is well-known London with its black and white colours simulating a racetrack ambience that appeals to the many bikers who regularly meet here at weekends. There is quite a buzz as bikers of all nationalities and ages swop information and stories, but the café also has a wider customer base, including local workers, seniors (in touch with their biking youth) and others just passing by who fancy a decent breakfast, lunch or snack.

Food is café style and a new menu has just been introduced. Good helpings at reasonable prices – bangers and mash are a favourite. A full range of drinks is available at usual pub prices.

OPENING TIMES
Mon-Sat: 07.00 - 23.00
Sun;
Public holidays: 07.00 - 22.30

FACILITIES
Disabled facilities
Newspapers
Cash machine: cash back
Parking: cars: 25
Caravans/coaches welcome

FOOD AND DRINK
Seating: 90
Daily specials
Vegetarian menu
Alcoholic beverages

Airport Café

A20 Main Road, Sellinge, Ashford TN25 6DA

Tel: 01303 813185

Directions: Leave the M20 at Junction 11 and follow the A20 west for one and a half miles. After Lympne Racecourse on the right, look for a white building with a green roof – this is the Airport Café.

With its distinctive green tiled roof, the Airport Café is easy to find. It has been in business for many years when it was owned by Mrs Breen's parents (the present owner). The building originated in the 1930s when the A20 was the main road from London to Folkestone and Hythe.

The café is quite small but is obviously a popular stopping place and has a constant stream of customers calling in for breakfast. As well as the standard menu, there are changing daily specials such as roast beef and Yorkshire pudding with vegetables and gravy £3.75, ham salad and new potatoes £3.20 and jam roly-poly and custard (or cream) £2.65. For truckers who want to wash their trucks, ask at the counter. There is a truck wash locally.

OPENING TIMES

Mon-Fri: 08.00 - 15.00
Sat: 08.00 - 12.00 noon
Sun;
Public holidays: Closed

FACILITIES

Newspapers: read only
Parking: cars: 20 trucks: 30
Caravans welcome
Coaches: advance notice required

FOOD AND DRINK

Seating: 33
Daily specials
Kids' menu
Vegetarian menu
No alcoholic beverages

No credit cards

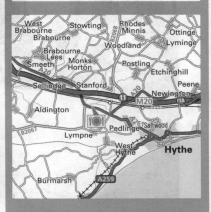

Autostop Cafe

113 Cambridge Road, Wimpole, Nr Royston S98 5QB

Tel: 01223 207370

Directions: From exit 12 on M11 take A603 for Cambridge in the direction of Royston. The Autostop Café is on the left hand side before the roundabout with the A1198.

The Autostop Café is very busy even though on a quietish road. It is a popular stopping place for locals and truckers alike.

Ken Potter, the owner, has been at the café for 16 years and knows exactly what his customers want: traditional English food with fast and friendly service! The set breakfast of egg, bacon, sausage, fried slice, tomatoes or beans is £3.40, and the 'full house', with fried potatoes, is £4.00. Tea and coffee are extra. Another favourite is gammon steak with chips, peas and an egg at £5.10. There's also a good selection of omelettes as well as fresh and toasted sandwiches. The dessert board – definitely worth a look – includes favourites such as spotted dick, fruit crumbles and pies with custard or ice cream, for £1.95.

There's a sunny, enclosed patio away from the road at the rear with tables and chairs for the summer months.

OPENING TIMES

Mon-Fri:	07.00 - 16.00
Sat:	07.00 - 14.00
Sun;	
Public holidays:	Closed

FACILITIES

Washroom for drivers
Parking: cars: plenty; trucks: 5
Caravans welcome
Coaches: no
Garden: patio

FOOD AND DRINK

Seating: 48
Outdoor eating area
Daily specials
No alcoholic beverages

No credit cards

Avon Forest Café

Brocks Pine, St Leonards, Ringwood BH24 2DH

Tel: 01425 471641

Directions: A31 east of Ringwood, at St Leonards. Brocks Pine, Avon Park signed southbound off roundabout.

This café provides a peaceful stop in the Avon Forest Country Park, 540 acres of park and woodland on the edge of the New Forest. This is a busy modern café that has a large outdoor eating area and is ideal for families. Normal café foods are available such as breakfasts, burgers, pasta dishes and pies as well as ice creams, snacks, sweets and so on, and the staff are friendly.

With plenty of parking space this is also an overnight truck stop, which is floodlit. There are public conveniences and public telephones, and tourist information is also available here. Information boards show flower and fauna you can expect to see here, and also gives routes for walks and rambles on different nature trails.

OPENING TIMES

Mon-Thu:	08.00 - 20.00
Fri-Sat:	08.00 - 18.00
Sun:	09.00 - 17.00
Public holidays:	Closed

FACILITIES

Disabled facilities
Newspapers
Parking: cars: 100; trucks: 30
Security: lighting
Caravans welcome
Coaches: advance notice required
Garden
Children's play area

FOOD AND DRINK

Seating: 50
Outdoor eating area
Daily specials, Kids' menu
Vegetarian menu
No alcoholic beverages

No credit cards

Bannisters

A22 Eastbourne Road, Blindley Heath RH7 6LQ
Tel: 01342 832086

Directions: Main A22 route to Eastbourne from M25. Close to East Grinstead and just beyond the village of Blindley Heath. Close to Lingfield Park racecourse. Well signposted at location.

Bannisters is a family-run business incorporating tearooms, a restaurant museum and shop – a great place to stop.

The bakery shop, decorated with teapots from all over the world has, a wonderful array of preserves and homemade cakes and buns and breads for sale. An original delivery boy's bicycle, with basket, hangs on the wall.

The charming and warm tearoom houses an original 18th-century faggot oven and a 19th-century side flue oven for the bakery.

The restaurant serves English breakfasts at £6.75, plus sandwiches, rolls and ploughmans. Cheese scones with filling are £1.95; Welsh rarebit on 2 toasts cost £3.95. The main menu includes many favourites like steak and kidney pie, macaroni cheese - all served with salad and potatoes - in the £7.00 range. Outside is a pretty courtyard with tables and chairs and a tiny fountain.

OPENING TIMES
Tue-Fri:	09.00 - 17.00
Sat:	09.00 - 18.00
Sun:	11.00 - 18.00
Public holidays:	Closed

FACILITIES
Disabled facilities
Parking: cars: plenty;
 trucks: a few
Garden

FOOD AND DRINK
Seating: 32
Outdoor eating area
Kids' menu
Vegetarian menu
No alcoholic beverages
Credit cards charged under £15.00

Boss Hoggs Transport Café

London Road, Copdock, Ipswich IP8 3JW

Tel: 01473 730797

Directions: Accessible from both carriageways of A12. Exit at Junction 32b and follow signs for Copdock. The truckstop is on the right. The Queen Elizabeth Hotel is nearby.

Over the years, Boss Hoggs Transport Café has transformed from bungalow to truckstop to café and now, owned by Mrs Humphreys, retains the look of its predecessor, Little Chef, with a long counter and wood-panelled walls. There is ample parking space at the rear – though it is uneven – and access is easy from both carriageways of the A12.

A typical item on the menu: steak and kidney pie, vegetables and gravy.

This is John Constable country. The subjects of two of his most famous paintings – Flatford Mill and Dedham Vale, are within a few miles of Boss Hoggs.

OPENING TIMES

Mon-Fri:	07.00 - 15.00
Sat-Sun:	
Public holidays:	Closed

FACILITIES

Newspapers
Parking: cars: 20; trucks: 20, no overnight parking
Caravans/coaches welcome

FOOD AND DRINK

Seating: 40
Daily specials
Kids' menu
Vegetarian menu
No alcoholic beverages

No credit cards

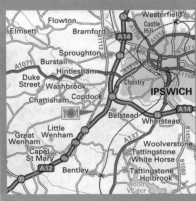

Bungalow Café

A12 (B1408), 45 London Road (Old A12), Marks Tey, Colchester CO6 1EB
Tel: 01206 210242

Directions: Exit A12 at Junction 25 then follow B1408 for Colchester. Truckstop is on the right.

The Bungalow Café has been a popular eating place for over 60 years. Although predominantly a truckstop, the café has a lot of support locally and has become a regular eating place for business lunches.

Owned by Nigel Holland, the café has recently been refurbished inside and is clean and light. In one corner there are shelves of books that customers can use to exchange for others.

In the past the café was used regularly by pop groups (among them the Rolling Stones), who found it a good place to stop off at on the way to gigs. It is now a regular stopping point for motorcyclists wanting a cup of tea after a 'ride-out'. Specials include egg and bacon pie with potatoes, peas and gravy.

OPENING TIMES

Mon-Thu:	06.00 - 18.00
Fri:	06.00 - 16.00
Sat:	07.30 - 15.00
Sun; Public holidays:	Closed

FACILITIES

Newspapers: read only
Parking: cars: 60; trucks: 18, overnight £2.50
Caravans/coaches welcome

FOOD AND DRINK

Seating: 60
Daily specials
Vegetarian menu
No alcoholic beverages

No credit cards

The Cabin Café

Crawley Road, Faygate, Nr Horsham RH12 4SC
Tel: 01293 851575

Directions: Leave M23 at Junction 11 Pease Pottage – travel along A264. Cabin Café is sited three miles from motorway junction, on the Faygate roundabout.

Easy to spot with its bright blue signage and teapot painted on to white walls, the café looks bright and inviting. The same can be said for the interior, with its bright blue and white gingham curtains.

The friendly welcome on arrival is quite genuine; the café is run by the third generation of the Webber family. The café has been featured in the *Sunday Times* and was also awarded 'best truckstop' in the Scania book. Breakfasts are big business. The weekly consumption of breakfast ingredients ran to 120 dozen eggs, 81 kilos of bacon, 800 sausages, 95 kilos of baked beans and 2,000 teabags! Thick bacon sandwiches are made with wonderfully fresh white cottage loaves, and there are other tempting meals to choose from.

Overnight parking for truckers Monday to Thursday is £10.00, which includes an evening meal and tea or coffee.

OPENING TIMES
Mon-Thu:	06.30 - 19.00
Fri:	06.30 - 13.00
Sat:	07.00 - 11.30
Sun;	
Public holidays:	Closed

FACILITIES
Disabled facilities
Washroom for drivers
Newspapers
Parking: cars: plenty; trucks: plenty, overnight £10 inc. evening meal
Coaches welcome
Children's play area

FOOD AND DRINK
Seating: 50
Outdoor eating area
Daily specials
Kids' menu
Vegetarian menu
No alcoholic beverages

No credit cards

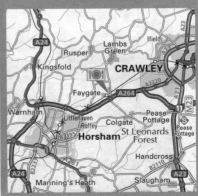

The Chalet Café

Henfield Road, Cowfold, Nr Horsham RH13 8DU
Tel: 01403 864314

Directions: Off the A272 to Haywards Heath, take A281 to Cowfold (Henfield Road). Chalet Café is set back at the end of the village.

In a picturesque setting outside the village of Cowfold, the Chalet Café is very popular with families, motorcyclists and the 'Smart Car Club', who meet there every weekend. It is also a regular stopping place for the local constabulary – which certainly makes for interesting stories. Allen Howes, the owner for the last 16 years, recounts incidents of bikers doing wheelies in full view of the police! A ticket ordering system operates here, as all the meals are prepared to order and delivered to your table quickly, and with a smile. The all-day set breakfast costs £4.00. Even without 'options' it looks more than adequate. On the menu are black pudding, hash browns, bubble and squeak, and other wonderful old English dishes that are making a popular comeback. It's interesting to note that visitors want these old favourites back on menus – a great change from the everyday fast-food options.

OPENING TIMES

Mon-Fri: 07.00 - 14.00
Sat: 07.00 - 13.30
Sun;
Public holidays: 08.00 - 13.00

FACILITIES

Washroom for drivers
Newspapers
Parking: cars: plenty;
trucks: open area
Caravans/coaches welcome
Garden

FOOD AND DRINK

Seating: 60
Outdoor eating area
Daily specials
Kids' menu
Vegetarian menu
No alcoholic beverages

No credit cards

Chatteris Café/Green Welly Motel

2A Doddington Road, Chatteris PE16 6UA
Tel: 01354 695490
Directions: A141 March to Chatteris Road, on roundabout of A141/142 Ely. The motel is on Doddington Road by the roundabout.

Maria Hobbs, who owns and runs this small independent family budget hotel, has plenty to be happy about: it's the fishing season and fishermen from all over the UK come to stay at her motel, hence the name 'Green Welly'. Also used daily by farmers and locals, Maria's busy café serves favourites like homemade toad-in-the-hole, chilli con carne with rice at £3.50 and 250g steak, chips and peas at £4.60. She uses as much local produce as possible. Breakfasts are served all day and cost £3.20, which includes a cup of tea. There is a small charge for coffee. In the bar you can buy draught and bottled beers, wines and spirits.

On the café wall is a very large Ordnance Survey map showing the local rivers where fishing competitions take place. The fishing theme is carried through to the licensed bar with pictures of coarse fish on the walls.

OPENING TIMES
Mon-Sun:
Public holidays: Closed

FACILITIES
Disabled facilities
Washroom for drivers
Newspapers
Parking: cars/trucks: plenty
Caravans/coaches welcome

ACCOMMODATION
12 Doubles/twins: £20.00; ensuite £24.00
2 Singles: from £12.00
2 Family: £30.00

FOOD AND DRINK
Seating: 44
Outdoor eating area
Daily specials; Kids' menu
Alcoholic beverages

No credit cards

Chris' Café Motel

Wycombe Road, Studley Green, High Wycombe HP14 3XB
Tel: 01494 482121

Directions: Chris' Motel is on the north side, west of the A4010. Exit M40 at either Junction 4 or 5, and take A40, two miles from High Wycombe. It is opposite West Wycombe Motors.

This is predominantly a truckers' stop, although other road users do use the café. The food is wholesome with meat stews, pies and roasts plus lots of vegetables and potatoes with gravy, all good, nourishing foods – nothing is left on any of the plates after a meal, which says it all.

Lydia, the manageress, knows her customers well, as the café has a loyal and regular following. One of her titled neighbours comes in regularly for his special plate of gammon, chips and mushy peas – says it's the best in the country.

The motel has 35 single rooms for truckers for £20.00 a night – which includes an evening meal, bed and breakfast. Overnight parking at £9.00 per night includes an evening meal in the café with a pudding and 2 cups of tea. This has to be the best value overnight deal around. There's also a TV room for overnight drivers.

OPENING TIMES
Mon-Thu: 06.00 - 19.00
Fri: 06.00 - 14.00
Sat: 06.30 - 12.00 noon
Sun: Closed

FACILITIES
Washroom for drivers
Cash machine
Parking: cars: plenty; trucks: open space, overnight £9.00 inc. evening meal

ACCOMMODATION
35 Single: £20.00 (p.p.) bed/breakfast/evening meal

FOOD AND DRINK
Seating: 30
Kids' menu
No alcoholic beverages

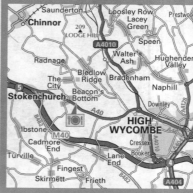

The Clock Tower Café

3 The High Street, Newmarket CB8 8LX
Tel: 01638 663303

Directions: Enter the town of Newmarket and head for the centre. The Clock Tower is situated at the east end of the High Street, opposite the Clock Tower.

The Clock Tower Café is well known amongst the racing fraternity – from stable lads to owners, racing reporters, television interviewers and punters, reflected in the watercolour prints, photos and books that are displayed there, together with a variety of golfing and tennis memorabilia.

The café has large glass-fronted windows and is bright and cheerful. Stools at the window look out onto the Clock Tower, otherwise there are tables and chairs, and a few tables outside. Breakfasts are served all day, with either the working man's or a vegetarian choice, priced from £3.90 including toast and hot drink. There's a variety of toast toppings, sandwiches and buns as well. Owner Larry provides a basic menu but it is excellent, reasonably priced, freshly made and happily served. Don't be tempted to park on the double yellow lines in front of the café, there's plenty of car and truck parking nearby.

OPENING TIMES
Mon-Fri: 06.00 - 14.00
Sat, Sun;
Public holidays: Closed

FACILITIES
Newspapers: racing papers only
Parking: cars/trucks: nearby

FOOD AND DRINK
Seating: 36
Outdoor eating area
Daily specials
Vegetarian menu
No alcoholic beverages

No credit cards

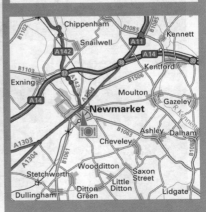

The Comfort Café

Fourwentwayn Services Area, Little Abington CB1 6AP
Tel: 01223 837891

Directions: The café is behind the 'Services' signed on the A11/A1307 roundabout.
Find the Little Chef, then continue round. The sign is 'Comfort Café'.

The Comfort Café is sometimes known as the World Famous Comfort Café. Owned by Daniel Hannan, it is very smart, with a vast menu and in the summer, music on the terrace. motorcycle rallies, vintage American car meetings and boot sales are held here and there's also an annual garden show in a marquee on the lawn. Anglia TV has filmed the café with the presenter Brian Turner for the series *A Taste of Anglia*.

On the burger menu you'll find the classics plus 'Pedro a Tex-Mex Chicken Burger', 'Sam the Ham' Burger and 'Perky the Pig Burger' all between £2 and £3.50. From the amazing kids' menu they can choose meals like "Proper Grub for Fussy Kids', "Food for Healthy Kids", or "Lighter Snacks for Little People". The vegetarian menu includes seafood options, omelettes and soups plus more substantial offerings.

A function room can be hired for private parties.

OPENING TIMES
Mon-Sun;
Public holidays: 07.30 - 20.30
(summer 22.00)

FACILITIES
Disabled facilities
Newspapers
Cash machine: cash back
Parking: cars: 60; trucks: 10
Security: CCTV
Caravans/coaches welcome
Garden
Children's play area

FOOD AND DRINK
Seating: 188
Outdoor eating area: 180
Daily specials
Kids' menu
Vegetarian menu
Alcoholic beverages

Crawley Crossing Truckstop

A507/A421 Bedford Road, Husborne Crawley MK43 0UT
Tel: 01908 281084

Directions: Leave the M1 at Junction 13. Take signs for A507 towards Aspley. Go over the roundabout and the truckstop is on the left.

The truckstop will seat about 50 people and provides a fairly extensive menu. Most of the lorry driver's favourites will be found here. A light breakfast is £3.80 and a cup of tea is 55p. The 'specials' include cottage pie, chips and peas £4.50 followed by apple sponge and custard £1.85. With any main meal of £4.00 or over, the dessert course costs only £1.00. Truckers find this an ideal compound in which to refuel (card payments only) and as the area is secured and fenced, it provides drivers with a secure overnight parking facility. This costs £6.00 and includes a shower and a £2.00 voucher for food. A shop on site provides for many driver's requirements.

Caravans and coaches are not admitted at the Crawley Crossing Truckstop, as the area is geared almost entirely to the accommodation of trucks, with some parking allocated to cars. Richardson's Catering owns the truckstop.

OPENING TIMES

Mon:	07.00 - 22.00
Tues -Thu:	06:00 - 22:00
Fri:	06:00 - 20:00
Sat:	07:00 - 12.00
Sun; Public holidays:	Closed

FACILITIES

Washroom for drivers
Parking: cars: 20; trucks: 40, £6.00 (£2.00 voucher)
Security: Lit

FOOD AND DRINK

Seating: 50
Daily specials
No alcoholic beverages

No credit cards

Dickie's Restaurant & Olive's Bar

A14 Eastbound, Orwell Crossing, Nacton IP10 0DD
Tel: 01473 659140   Fax: 01473 659148

Directions: A14 south of Ipswich, exit at Junction 57 or 58. The Orwell Crossing truckstop is immediately next to McDonalds, but has its own entrance. Dickie's & Olive's are well signed.

This new venture, opened in 2004, has taken the Rout family (ex farmers) by surprise, because at weekends and special holidays this brand new purpose-built restaurant and bar is usually fully booked.

The modern building is light, with central atrium, which has a sculpture water feature; an open reception/security desk and small convenience shop.

In the large carvery of Dickie's Restaurant professional chefs use local fresh ingredients where possible for the roasts; liver and bacon, or chicken dishes at £6.95 and a range of exciting choices that appear on the menu. There are also fish dishes; homemade soups; salads and fresh daily specials, and of course, drivers' breakfasts from £2.99. There is a New World wine list.

Olive's Bar serves draft and bottled beer, as well as spirits and wines. There's a large TV screen for sport enthusiasts, a pool table, and live music on Thursday and Saturday evenings.

OPENING TIMES
Mon-Sun: 24 hours

FACILITIES
Disabled facilities
Shower rooms for drivers: £2.50
Newspapers
Parking: cars/trucks: plenty
Security: CCTV 24 hours
Caravans/coaches welcome

FOOD AND DRINK
Seating: 300
Outdoor eating area
Daily specials
Kids' menu
Vegetarian menu
Alcoholic beverages

Foodstop Express

Tothill Service Station, Stowmarket IP14 3QQ
Tel:01449 616387
Directions: Eastbound on A14 from Stowmarket before Junction 49.
Alongside the BP petrol station.

This restaurant, with its bright, light green furniture, is clean, fresh and airy. It has a definite family atmosphere and it is obviously child friendly, with a number of high chairs and a toy box in evidence. A kids' menu contains the usual chicken nuggets and beef burgers, as well as 'surprise' ice cream cones selling at £2.99. There is also a small gift and toy counter.

Other items on the main menu are huge burgers at £4.50, vegetarian meals at £3.95, and homemade lasagne. In fact, something for everyone, plus all-day breakfasts.

Run by manageress Nicola Calvert, it is a busy café – at weekends there's the usual flow of day-trippers and travellers. It's also a popular meeting place for motorbike enthusiasts during the summer months when there are tables to sit at outside the front of the café.

OPENING TIMES

Mon-Thu:	08.00 - 15.00
Fri:	08.00 - 18.00
Sat-Sun:	08.00 - 16.00

FACILITIES

Newspapers
Parking: cars/trucks: plenty
Caravans/coaches welcome

FOOD AND DRINK

Seating: 35
Outdoor eating area
Daily specials
Kids' menu
Vegetarian menu
No alcoholic beverages

No credit cards

Four Oaks Café

173 New Road (A1306), Rainham RM13 8SH
Tel: 01708 552180

Directions: Leave M25 at Junction 30 and head for Dagenham/Rainham on the A13. Take the A1306 north. The Four Oaks is opposite the Rainham Steel Building.

When looking for the Four Oaks Café, don't expect to see trees! This is an industrial area with very little in the way of greenery.
As with many truckstops, the café was originally on a busy main road, but has now been by-passed. Truckers, though, have remained loyal and still use it as a regular stop-off.
Run by Alan and Joe for the last four years, the café's main customers are now from the various businesses and workshops in the local area. There is a varied choice of specials on the board including scampi and chips for £4.00; roasts or pork chops; chips and peas £4.40 amongst others.
There is a TV room and a licensed bar club next door.
Parking is fine for cars but trucks are a bit restricted.

OPENING TIMES
Mon-Fri:	07.00 - 19.00
Sat:	08.00 - 13.00
Sun:	08.15 - 12.00
Public holidays:	Closed

FACILITIES
Washroom for drivers
Newspapers
Parking: cars: 20; trucks: 5 overnight £5.00
Security: 24-hour caretaker
Caravans/coaches welcome

ACCOMMODATION
4 Singles; 4 Doubles;
3 Family: £15.00 (p.p.)

FOOD AND DRINK
Seating: 80
Daily specials; Kids' menu
Vegetarian menu
No alcoholic beverages
No credit cards

Fox's Diner

Oxford Road, Berinsfield Roundabout, Dorchester OX10 7LY
Tel: 01865 341607

Directions: From A34 Oxford to Abingdon – A415 Berinsfield roundabout at junction with A4074, or from M40 Junction 7, A329 to Shillingford, then right to next roundabout on A4074.

This famous bikers' stop was taken over 18 months ago by Jason Davenport and continues to be a successful café. Situated next to M & P Motorcycle Accessories, with a large hard surface forecourt in front of the diner, as well as picnic tables and chairs, it is a natural meeting place for motorbike enthusiasts. Inside, the diner is attractive, with a large open fireplace the length of the end wall and tables with red and white and blue and white tablecloths.

Occasionally there's a hog roast cooked and served outside. Otherwise, the menu has good home-cooked dishes, hot or cold, including substantial breakfasts, snacks and lunches. All-day breakfasts start at £5.00 with tea and coffee; 'The Works' breakfast is £6.00. Omelettes, soups, sandwiches and doorstops with a variety of delicious fillers are listed on a board, together with puddings and hot malted drinks.

OPENING TIMES
Mon: 08.00 - 21.00
Tue-Sun;
Public holidays: 08.00 - 18.00

FACILITIES
Disabled facilities
Newspapers
Cash back
Parking: cars/trucks: plenty
Caravans/coaches welcome

FOOD AND DRINK
Seating: 50
Outdoor eating area
Daily specials
Kids' menu
Vegetarian menu
No alcoholic beverages

George's Diner

361-363 North Woolwich Road, Silvertown E16 2VS

Tel: 0207 476 2379

Directions: On A1020, directly opposite Thames Barrier car park, close to A13 East London – Docklands. London City Airport and Excel are all close by. Café has plenty of parking in front of it.

It's a joy to find a café in this newly developed Docklands area that has remained unchanged for 21 years. Run by Brian Pill, the café is full and friendly, with a mixed clientele. On the wall, you'll see photographs of the area before it was developed.

The food is excellent value for money. There are the usual breakfasts, plus T-bone steaks at £5.50, and amongst others, pork chops and homemade pies and pasties, all with veg, at £3.33. Scampi and chips, or chicken casserole will cost you £3.80, with steamed puddings and custard to follow which look delicious. However, Brian is wondering how much longer it will be before his plot is up for re-development. Those who have found this treasure hope it will be a long time yet.

OPENING TIMES

Mon-Fri:	06.00 - 19.00
Sat:	06.00 - 10.30
	(breakfast only)
Public holidays:	Closed

FACILITIES

Disabled facilities
Washroom for drivers
Newspapers
Parking: cars/trucks: on road
 or Thames Barrier car park
Caravans: no
Coaches welcome

FOOD AND DRINK

Seating: 50
Daily specials
Vegetarian menu
No alcoholic beverages

No credit cards

Hillside Café

A36, Codford, Nr Warminster BA12 OJ2
Tel: 01985 850712
Directions: On A303 about 12 miles west of Stonehenge, take A36 north –
Bath/Bristol road. After the village of Codford, Hillside Café is situated on east side. It
is well signposted.

The tablemats in the Hillside Café show a photograph of how the café was when the present owners took over the premises over 30 years ago. Alongside is a photograph of it today – a purpose-built roadside café.
Ian and Terry Stock believe in looking after their customers. Ian prepares the food, while Terry happily runs the front of house. The café is well worth a detour of a couple of miles off the busy A303 for an excellent meal.
Breakfast starts at 06.00 everyday. The bacon is delicious – locally supplied – and fresh Kona coffee is available by the mug full. Prices between £2.70–£5.50. Roasts are very popular at £4.65 and are on the menu daily from 10.00 Another good dish is the homemade curry, and there's a good selection of fish dishes, all served with chips, peas or beans priced at £4.75. Salads, omelettes and sandwiches are also available.

Opening Times

Mon-Thu:	06.00 - 19.00
Fri:	06.00 - 17.00
Sat:	06.00 - 11.45
Sun; Public holidays:	Closed

Facilities

Disabled facilities
Newspapers
Parking: cars/trucks: plenty
Caravans/coaches welcome

Food and Drink

Seating: 50
Outdoor eating area
Daily specials
Kids' menu
Vegetarian menu
No alcoholic beverages

No credit cards

Hilltop Café

A14/A134 Rougham Hill, Bury St Edmunds IP33 2RU
Tel: 07904 464026

Directions: Exit A14 at Junction 44 (Sudbury A134). Follow truck park signs. Café sign is written inside a truck frame on the exterior wall.

This is a modern, purpose-built café, owned for ten years by Michael Walker who, with his staff, make a friendly team. The café is used mainly by trucks going to the east coast ports, as well as other drivers and travellers. Inside, there are pictures of big American trucks on the walls, and there's a TV and some fruit machines for relaxation.

All-day special breakfasts cost £3.70. The 'big boys' steaks – a 12oz (340g) T-bone at £6.20 and an 8oz (250g) sirloin steak at £4.95, with lots of potatoes and a selection of vegetables all included in the price – are a fantastic bargain. Michael's menu also gives a choice of good English traditional main courses and puddings.

In the large parking area are public conveniences and a public telephone.

The truck park is not fenced but it has 24-hour CCTV surveillance.

OPENING TIMES
Mon-Fri: 06.30 - 20.00
Sat: 07.00 - 12.00 noon
Sun; Public holidays: Closed

FACILITIES
Disabled facilities
Washroom for drivers
Newspapers
Parking: cars/trucks: plenty
Security: CCTV only open area
Caravans/coaches welcome

FOOD AND DRINK
Seating: 70
Daily specials
Vegetarian menu
No alcoholic beverages

No credit cards

Hilltop Grill

A30 London Road, Firsdown, Salisbury SP5 1ST
Tel: 01980 863086

Directions: A30 between Andover and Salisbury. Two miles before Salisbury, on south side of road before the turning for Firsdown. Well signposted and alongside Spire Care Sales.

Dayan will give you a flamboyant welcome to this pleasant and nicely decorated grill restaurant, making one feel immediately at home.

The menu, as the name would suggest, concentrates on grilled food but also has some tempting alternatives listed – a Sunday favourite is the Hilltop Roast Platter. There are also traditional roasts served with Yorkshire puddings and all the trimmings and cold snacks like a local Wiltshire ham baguette. The Grill is licensed to serve alcohol and has a good basic wine list to choose from to enjoy with your meal.

Available for hire for private functions, the Grill has plenty of car parking spaces.

Nearby are some beautiful country walks into the Wiltshire countryside along a Roman Road, and the cathedral city of Salisbury is well worth a visit. Owned by Mr Wells, the Hilltop Grill makes a perfect stop.

OPENING TIMES
Mon-Thu:	08.00 - 18.00
Fri-Sun:	08.00 - 19.00
Public holidays:	08.00 - 18.00
	(if a Mon)
Xmas:	Closed

FACILITIES
Disabled facilities
Newspapers
Parking: car/trucks
Caravans: welcome
Coaches: advance notice required

FOOD AND DRINK
Seating: 84
Daily specials
Kids' menu
Vegetarian menu
Alcoholic beverages

Jack's Hill Café

A5 Watling Street, Towcester NN12 8ET
Tel: 01327 350522

Directions: Head north on the A5 from the A5/A43 roundabout north of Towcester. Jack's Hill Café is 200 yards (182 metres) on the left.

Jack's Hill Café was originally called Pomfret House, a slightly Art Deco house belonging to the Hesketh family (famous for the motorcycles of the 1980s).

Silverstone racetrack is just up the road, and on race days the forecourt is full of motorists and motorcyclists going to or from the races.

In addition to the large dining area the café has a pub-sized bar with a pool table and TV. The menu includes chicken, lasagne, large Yorkshires with mince, all around £4.00, plus a wide selection of traditional desserts like sponge puddings and crumbles costing £1.20.

Jack's Hill Café, owned by John Capella, is well known and has been used as a backdrop for Jeremy Clarkson's *Top Gear* and was the venue for an edition of the Channel 4's *Scrapheap Challenge*. A celebrity chef spent the day here too, cooking meals.

Also on site are a motorists' shop and repair garage.

OPENING TIMES
Mon-Fri:	06.00 - 21.30
Sun:	
Public holidays:	07.00 - 14.30

FACILITIES
Disabled facilities
Washroom for drivers
Newspapers
Cash machine
Parking: cars: 50; trucks: 50, overnight £5.00, refrigerated
Caravans welcome

ACCOMMODATION
1 Double; 1 Single; 1 Family: £10.00 (p.p.)

FOOD AND DRINK
Seating: 80
Daily specials; Kids' menu
Vegetarian menu
Alcoholic beverages
No credit cards

Jean's Café

Canterbury Road, Boughton under Blean, Faversham ME13 8JU

Directions: 200 yards along the A2 after Junction 7 of the M2 – heading east. Serves eastbound traffic. It can also be accessed via a slip road by westbound traffic.

Jean's is a prefabricated cabin behind a lay-by a quarter of a mile from the M2 /A2/ A299 roundabout. Jean's has been on this site for 18 years and during those years she's experienced many events: on one occasion she arrived early to open up and found a Parisian flea circus camped out in sleeping bags waiting for a morning cup of tea! On another, a chauffeur-driven Daimler pulled up. The chauffeur ordered two bacon buns and two cafetières of coffee. It seems the Queen Mother was due to be at a ceremony at Deal (as warden of the Cinque Ports), but due to illness was not able to attend. There was great debate as to just whose royal arm it was in the car!

Jean's serves standard café food and there are no specials on offer. However she will take orders for just about anything and cooks to order!

OPENING TIMES
Mon-Fri: 07.30 - 16.00
Sat, Sun:
Public holidays: Closed

FACILITIES
Parking: cars: 10: trucks: 8
Caravans/coaches welcome

FOOD AND DRINK
Seating: 25
Outdoor eating area
Kids' menu
Vegetarian menu
No alcoholic beverages

No credit cards

69

John's Cross Café

A21 Robertsbridge TN32 5JJ
Tel: 01580 881911

Directions: John's Cross Café is on the A21 Tunbridge Wells to Hastings road, about two miles south of the roundabout for Robertsbridge. It is on the west side of the road.

John's Cross Café is a pleasant recently refurbished roadside truckstop/café, south of Hurst Green. The present owner, Jayne Shilton, has been here for a year and seen a monthly increase in the number of customers. Many of these are working people who call in for breakfast, travellers who stop for lunch, people out for a drive, or local pensioners in for their main meal of the day.

Specials include ribs in barbeque sauce, roast lamb shank and homemade curry of the day. These are generally priced between £5.50 and £6.00. There is a fully licensed bar.

The original 1930s building was a garage and workshop, but has since had several incarnations. Just before its present role, it was an Indian restaurant, which is hinted at by the lighting and carpet that remain.

John's Cross Café also caters for weddings, parties and other functions.

OPENING TIMES
Mon-Sat: 07.00 - 19.00
Sun: 08.00 - 16.00
Public holidays: Closed

FACILITIES
Disabled facilities
Newspapers: read only
Parking: cars: 20; trucks: 6
Caravans welcome
Coaches: advance notice required
Garden

FOOD AND DRINK
Seating: 80
Outdoor eating area
Daily specials
Kids' menu
Vegetarian menu
Alcoholic beverages

Jungle Café

A20/M20 London Road, Addington, West Malling ME19 5PL
Tel: 01732 842020

Directions: Jungle Café is on the A20 west of Ditton. From the M20, leave at Junction 4 and head south along the A228. At the junction with the A20, turn right, heading west. The café is two miles along the road on the left.

The Jungle Café is a busy café built about ten years ago. Mr Diaz, who has owned the café for 25 years, renamed it the Jungle Café to reflect past times when this was the only stopping place in the area and was surrounded by trees and greenery.

Mr Diaz is responsible for the friendliness and efficiency of the place. The family, originally from Spain, are all now in the business with mother, father and two sons working together. The specials change daily, and include homemade chicken and vegetable pie, £3.95; braised steak, £3.75 and also a range of homemade pastries.

The parking area in the front is quite small by truckstop standards, but appears to accommodate all those who stop to eat. The café has a pool table and gaming machine for amusement.

OPENING TIMES

Mon-Fri:	07.00 - 15.00
Sat:	07:00 - 12.00
Sun; Public holidays:	Closed

FACILITIES

Newspapers
Parking: cars: 15; trucks: 10
Caravans/coaches welcome

FOOD AND DRINK

Seating: 60
Kids' menu
Vegetarian menu
No alcoholic beverages

No credit cards

Kelly's Diner

A43 Kettering Road, Hannington, Northampton NN6 9TB
Tel: 01604 780378

Directions: Kelly's Diner is between Northampton and Kettering on the A43. It is behind the Shell services at the crossroads leading to Isham.

Previously a café but now a diner, Kelly's has re-opened with pleasantly decorated interior, with separate area for smokers, and pine tables and bright red covered chairs.

The entrance has a new service bar with espresso coffee machine, giving a wonderful aroma as you enter the diner. Katherine, the new owner, runs the café with her daughter Kelly. It's a favourite meeting place for bikers, particularly at weekends.

On the menu are the all-day breakfasts at £5.25 including the coffee and tea. or mega breakfast for £6.50. Or you can try anything you like – you choose – they cook it! Also available are starters, grills, chicken fillet burgers and gammon between £6.00 and £9.00. Other meals are lamb shanks; rack of ribs; chef's chilli and Kelly's curry, plus vegetarian tuna pasta bake, and to finish, a selection of puddings.

OPENING TIMES
Mon-Fri: 08.00 - 17.00
Sat-Sun;
Public holidays: 08.00 - 15.00

FACILITIES
Disabled facilities
Newspapers
Parking: cars: plenty; trucks: limited
Caravans/coaches welcome
Garden

FOOD AND DRINK
Seating: 60
Outdoor eating area
Daily specials
Kids' menu
Vegetarian menu
No alcoholic beverages

No credit cards

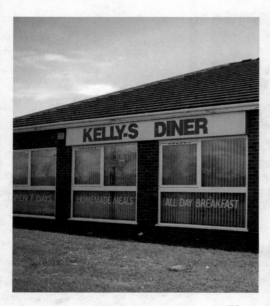

M's Family Diner

A33, Swallowfield by-pass, Reading RG7 1LZ
Tel: 01189 884026

Directions: M4 Junction 11 – take A33 towards Basingstoke. Three quarters of a mile south on dual carriageway, next to BP petrol station – use the same entrance.

Allan has been the proprietor at M's for the last three years. This diner certainly has a different menu to the normal roadside fare. There is a wide selection of fish dishes – cod, plaice and scampi – and his 'seafood combi salad' (£8.95) looks well worth a try. He also serves pizzas made to order and cooked on a wood-fired base (£5.00 + topping). Try ordering a special mix of the many toppings he has on offer. There's a discount for seniors. Sunday is a particularly busy day, when families come from Reading for the traditional roast lunches.

This air-conditioned restaurant is available for party bookings and family celebrations and Allan has a licence to sell alcohol.

There are a few framed oil paintings hanging on the wall that Allan sells to help support local artists.

In summer there is a patio with tables for outside eating.

OPENING TIMES

Tue-Thu:	07.00 - 16.00
Fri-Sun:	07.00 - 20.00

FACILITIES

Disabled facilities
Newspapers
Parking: cars/trucks: plenty, refrigerated spaces
Caravans/coaches welcome

FOOD AND DRINK

Seating: 100
Outdoor eating area
Daily specials
Kids' menu
Vegetarian menu
Alcoholic beverages

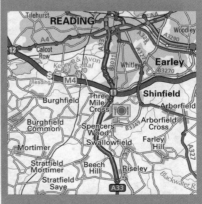

Marian's Diner

Lay-by, half mile off Bedford bypass on A6, Wilstead Road, Bedford
Tel: 078146 28930

Directions: Head off the Bedford bypass (A421) to go south on the A6. The diner is in a lay-by on the left.

Marian's Diner has been on the lay-by at Wilstead for four years. It is difficult to miss as it is painted bright yellow. It is a small coach fitted out to seat twelve people on high stools around the sides of the interior.

Marian doesn't have 'special' meals, but all available ingredients can be prepared to customers' requirements. A breakfast is £4.80, a cup of tea is 50p and a cup of coffee is 60p. There is a selection of home-baked cakes and tarts.

Owner Marian Burrows and her sister have had some interesting experiences here – one customer, a private detective asked Marian to help her catch a cheating husband. Another regular is a football talent scout.

There are no toilets on the lay-by, as they would be vandalised, but there is a garden centre further down the road with all facilities. Woburn Abbey is nearby and also the 17th-century house Chicheley Hall.

OPENING TIMES
Mon-Fri: 07.00 - 15.00
Sat-Sun;
Public holidays   Closed

FACILITIES
Newspapers: to read
Parking: in lay-by
Caravans/coaches welcome

FOOD AND DRINK
Seating: 12
Outdoor eating area
Kids' menu
Vegetarian menu
No alcoholic beverages

No credit cards

The Merrychest Café

A296/A2/M2, Watling Street, Bean
Tel: 01474 832371

Directions: Leave the A2 at signs for Bluewater then follow signs for A296 A2/M2.
Note for trucks: do NOT attempt to drive through Bean Village.

The Merrychest is on the old main road from London to Canterbury and Dover. It is a curious looking building to be seen by the roadside, resembling a cricket pavilion, with huge bay windows either end of the front façade. The interior is one huge room, so deep that the roof is constructed not of timber, but iron girders.

Originally this café was a tearoom serving people on their way to the Continent, and was ornately decorated with moulded ceilings, chandeliers and panelled walls. All that remains of these are the wall lights and some ceiling mouldings.

Now run by Tracey, Julie and Terry, the café serves all the favourites – breakfasts, main meals and salads – and 'specials' that include shepherds pie with vegetables, or liver and bacon at £4.25 and desserts like chocolate pudding or sponge pudding and custard at £2.00.

Opening Times

Mon-Fri:	06.30 - 17.00
	(Wed closes 22.00,
	BBQ night)
Sat:	06.30 - 12.00 noon
Sun;	
Public holidays:	Closed

Facilities

Disabled facilities
Newspapers
Parking: on road
Caravans/coaches welcome

Food and Drink

Seating: 60
Daily specials
Kids' menu
Vegetarian menu
No alcoholic beverages

No credit cards

Nell's Café

A2 Watling Street, Marling Cross, Gravesend DA12 5UD

Tel: 01474 362457

Directions: On the A2 between Gravesend and Rochester. Nell's is about two and a half miles beyond the A227 junction. Look out for a white building on a bank on the left. Only accessible to eastbound traffic.

Laurie Yeomans has owned Nell's Café for the last 22 years, although it originated in the 1940s. The café is very bright and airy with walls that are attractively half tiled and there is a collection of old advertising signs hanging above.

The café is well known to TV camera crews. It has been used for an episode of the Robson Green series and was lined up for filming by one of the main political parties in the 2005 General Election.

On the menu, daily specials include steak and kidney pudding with potatoes and vegetables for £5.20 and traditional desserts like apple pie or rhubarb crumble for £2.80.

Truck parking is on the opposite side of the slip road

OPENING TIMES

Mon-Fri: 06.30 - 22.00
Sat-Sun: 06.30 - 18.00
Public holidays: 08.00 - 17.00

FACILITIES

Washroom for drivers
Newspapers: to read
Parking: cars: 20; trucks: 20
Caravans/coaches welcome

FOOD AND DRINK

Seating: 55
Outdoor eating area
Daily specials
Kids' menu
Vegetarian menu
No alcoholic beverages

No credit cards

NT Truckstops

Rusts Lane, Alconbury, Huntingdon PE28 4DJ
Tel: 01480 454476

Directions: Exit A1(M) at Junction 14 (for A14). Follow sign for Alconbury on B1043. Lorry services signposted, entry next to service station and truckstop.

The services, run by Jackie Waters, include a good restaurant, a convenience shop, cash machine, fruit machines – as well as motel accommodation.

The light and airy restaurant has a canteen-style carvery, with an interesting selection of daily specials, for example sausage ring at £3.99; breaded lamb cutlets £4.49; vegetarian dishes at £3.99, as well as the usual extensive menu, plus the best selection of very good coffee.

The motel is alongside, with single and double rooms. There's a pleasant and quiet TV room, as well as a public bar, with a wide screen TV and a pool room, popular with drivers. In summer months, you can sit outside in the beer garden and eating area.

There is a truck wash in the parking compound.

OPENING TIMES
Mon 06.00 - Sat 12.00: 24 hours
Sun: 12.00 - 17.00
Public holidays: Closed

FACILITIES
Disabled facilities
Washroom for drivers
Newspapers; Cash machine
Parking: cars/trucks: plenty
Caravans welcome
Coaches: advance notice required. Garden

ACCOMMODATION
Doubles: ensuite: TV: £25.99
Singles: ensuite: TV: £19.99

FOOD AND DRINK
Seating: 120
Outdoor eating area
Daily specials; Kids' menu
Vegetarian menu
Alcoholic beverages (licensing hours)

Oakdene

A20 (M20/M26), London Road, Wrotham TN15 7RR
Tel: 01732 884873 Fax: 01732 84152

Directions: Leave M26 at Junction 2A and head for Wrotham. Oakdene is on the right after about half a mile.

The Oakdene first opened over 60 years ago and is one of the best-known cafés in the area. Mrs Jeavons the owner has run the place for about 23 years. The atmosphere is a bit like the bikers' cafés of the 1950s where they would call in for coffee and a chat and put notices on the board of bits and pieces for sale or wanted.

Customers can choose from a range of delicious looking homemade pastries, while specials range in price from £2.80 to around £4.50 and include homemade curry and homemade steak and kidney.

There is a large function room that is hired out for private parties – the local motorcycle club meets here twice a week and is involved in fund raising for the Kent Air Ambulance – over the years members have raised about £5,000. The American Car Club also meets here on the first Saturday of every month.

OPENING TIMES
Mon-Fri: 06.00 - 18.30
                  (Weds shuts 22.00)
Sat-Sun: 06.00 - 17.00
Public holidays   07.00 - 15.00
Xmas & New Year   Closed

FACILITIES
Disabled facilities
Newspapers
Parking: cars: 10; trucks: 25,
£5.00 per night, not Wed
Caravans/coaches welcome
Garden
Children's play area

FOOD AND DRINK
Seating: 80
Outdoor eating area
Daily specials
Kids' menu
Vegetarian menu
Alcoholic beverages
(restaurant licence)

Old Willoughby Hedge Café

A303 West Knoyle, Nr Salisbury
Tel: 01747 830803

Directions: On A303, between two long stretches of dual carriageway, west of A350. On a lay-by, going west directly after signage on road for toilets and food is Old Willoughby Hedge Café.

This café is so famous that it has become well known along the length of the A303. It's really just a Portakabin but it could not be missed out of this book because from June, 2005 it will be replaced by a brand new, modern unit. Dave Thomas has been the owner of this café since 1980 and he and his staff look forward to seeing the new unit in situ.

To date, the food that has always been freshly cooked to order, mostly local bacon, eggs, and sausages, in sandwiches or baps, to eat in or take away. Homemade local beef burgers, quarter pounders start at £1.60 with various extras as 50p each. More dishes will be added to the menu when the new unit arrives. There is also a small outside eating area. Situated in the lay-by are public toilets, as well as a baby-changing facility.

OPENING TIMES
Mon-Sun;
Public holidays: 08.00 - 18.00

FACILITIES
Disabled facilities
Parking: cars/trucks: lay-by

FOOD AND DRINK
Seating: 8
Outside eating area
Kids' menu
No alcoholic beverages

No credit cards

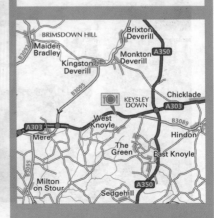

The Orchard Café

776 Staines Road, Bedfont, Hounslow TW14 8RU
Tel: 01784 258795

Directions: Exit the M25 at Junction 13 and take the A30 eastbound to London. Orchard Café is on the north side of the dual carriageway. It backs on to Heathrow airport.

Mr Mahida, who has been successfully running cafés for some years, took over this café in 2005.

It has been popular with truckers and locals for many years, and the atmosphere and style of the café has changed very little – it has a comfortable, aged feel to it with the old rotating ceiling fans and on the walls are framed, signed photos of TV stars who have eaten there, certificates of excellence and photographs of the BBC film crew's visit of 1993. It also has the old-style fruit and pinball machines, rarely seen nowadays.

Typical fare includes two breakfasts – the Big Breakfast at £3.90, and Regular at £2.50, plus breakfast sandwiches, burgers, and a great omelette menu with a variation of fillers to choose from starting at £1.60. Plenty of specials to choose from include lamb shank; roast chicken and cottage pie, starting at £5.80, including two vegetables.

OPENING TIMES
Mon-Fri:	07.00 - 14.00
Sat:	07.00 - 12.00 noon
Sun; Public holidays:	Closed

FACILITIES
Disabled facilities
Newspapers
Parking: cars/trucks: plenty

FOOD AND DRINK
Seating: 60
Daily specials
Kids' menu
Vegetarian menu
No alcoholic beverages

No credit cards

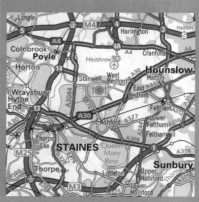

The Pantry

A45 Willoughby, Rugby CV23 8BL

Directions: From M45 Dunchurch junction, go south on A45 towards Daventry. In village of Willoughby halfway to Daventry, café is next to Four Crosses garage.

Roger and Margaret, the owners of The Pantry for the last eight years run a truly charming café. Not at all pretentious. With the square white tables and red chairs, blue and white decorative china plates hanging on the walls and a counter with fresh cakes, buns, fresh sandwiches, and Kona coffee simmering, what more do you need?

The atmosphere is easy and friendly and the staff good fun. Good cooked meals at the right prices come quickly from the kitchen with the usual breakfast choice of standard and jumbo from £2.60–£5.20 and daily specials including home-baked ham with chips, peas, salad and a bread roll at £4.50. Others on the board include steak and kidney pie; fresh mince pie; homemade shepherds pie or sausage and onions all reasonably priced around £4.00. Children have their own menu and there are several desserts, like crumbles and ice cream sundaes.

OPENING TIMES

Mon-Fri:	07.00 - 15.00
Sat-Sun:	07.00 - 14.00

FACILITIES

Disabled facilities
Parking: cars/trucks: plenty
Caravans/coaches welcome

FOOD AND DRINK

Seating: 50
Daily specials
Kids' menu
Vegetarian menu
No alcoholic beverages

No credit cards

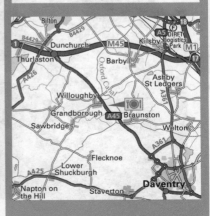

The Plough Inn

Waterside, Upton upon Severn WR8 0HY
Tel: 01684 593182

Directions: At M5, Junction 8, take M50 Junction 1, exit north up A38, and left in town of Upton upon Severn (A4104). Go over the bridge and take left turn, then left again on to the riverfront. The Plough Inn is at the water's edge. Parking for cars in front of the pub. Trucks are able to park at the nearby truckstop – over bridge, turn right and take the second turn on left.

Once on the river's edge, you will see on the corner the tables, chairs and red and black umbrellas of the Plough Inn which, though olde worlde, has become popular both with passing truckers and with locals. It has excellent food including a 'truckers menu'. The public bar has a pool table and TV screen. There is a comfortable eating area, and another area with easy chairs and low tables. Publican Justin and his partner Tracey look after the truckers well. Despite the inn being in the centre of town – an unusual stopping place for truckers – the drivers seem to like this spot although to park, they have to turn right immediately after the bridge and then left into the truck park a five-minute walk away.

Meals are wholesome and fresh produce is the key ingredient. Ploughmans, beef and chilli, double cheeseburgers, lasagne dishes are all about £3.95. Omelettes and salads are on offer as well.

OPENING TIMES
Mon-Fri: 06.30 - 20.30
Sat, Sun;
Public holidays: Closed

FACILITIES
Parking: cars: on street;
trucks: see description

FOOD AND DRINK
Seating: 40
Outdoor eating area
Daily specials
Kids' menu
Vegetarian menu
Alcoholic beverages

Portsmouth Truckstop Diner and Bar

Railway Triangle, Walton Road, Farlington, Portsmouth PO6 1UJ
Tel: 023 9237 6000

Directions: Take the turning off the A27 to Portsmouth (W), exit off the roundabout., immediately after the roundabout turn left at the Peugeot garage (opposite Shell petrol station). Follow signs to the Railway Triangle Industrial Estate/Ferry. Portsmouth Truckstop is on the right hand side of the road, about three minutes from the roundabout.

Owner Dave O'Donnell used to own a transport company in the area and, seeing the lack of cafés for drivers, he took over the Portsmouth Truckstop. Inside, the fresh blue upholstery, smart tables and pretty lace curtains belie the Portakabin exterior while outside, the patio is surrounded by plant pots and window boxes that give a cheerful look to the area.

You'll get a warm welcome from Lorraine behind the counter who presides over an extensive menu of well-priced meals that range from all-day breakfasts (£3.50 – £5.50, depending on how much of the full works you want!) through to a variety of specials. These might include beef curry and chips for £4.00 and traditional roasts and veg for £4.00, as well as a selection of puddings (£1.50). There's also a wide variety of items such as sandwiches (£1.80), soup and bread (£1.50) and salads. Tea and coffee are 50p.

OPENING TIMES
Mon-Thu:	05.00 - 21.00
Fri:	05.00 - 17.00
Sat;	
Public holidays:	07.00 - 14.00
Sun:	Closed

FACILITIES
Washroom for drivers
Launderette; Newspapers
Parking: cars: 30; trucks: 120, refrigerated trucks, £10.00 overnight
Diesel and Gasoil available with fuel cards
Security: lighting/patrolled/overnight CCTV, fenced
Caravans/coaches welcome

ACCOMMODATION
3 Singles; 2 Doubles: £14.00 (p.p.)

FOOD AND DRINK
Seating: 40
Outdoor eating area; Daily specials
Vegetarian menu
Alcoholic beverages
No credit cards

The Red Lion Pub Café

Junction 16, M1, Upper Heyford NN7 4DE
Tel: 01604 831914

Directions: The Red Lion is half a mile from Junction 16 of the M1, just off the westbound A4500 from Northampton. Heading east of the M1, the Red Lion can be accessed by turning right onto the westbound carriageway at the first right turn. It is on a slip road.

The Red Lion Pub Café is a public house and truckstop, the truckers' eating area being at the rear.

Owner Nigel Oddy has decorated the inside of the café with cartoon pictures, many by the Victorian cartoonist 'Spy', and some rare advertising signs – one from the 1930s for Royal Navy and Royal Marine recruits. Clues to the history of the building lie in the perfectly round indentations in some of the stone blocks of what had been an external wall. They appear to be the result of using the stones to sharpen something.

Special dishes at the café include roasts with all the trimmings and a selection of desserts, all served with cream or custard.

OPENING TIMES
Mon-Fri: 07.00 - 18.00
Sat-Sun: 08.00 - 16.00
Sun: 08.00 - 13.30
Public holidays: 08.00 - 14.00

FACILITIES
Newspapers
Parking: cars/trucks: plenty
Caravans/coaches welcome
Garden

FOOD AND DRINK
Seating: 60
Outdoor eating area
Daily specials
Kids' menu
Vegetarian menu
No alcoholic beverages

No credit cards

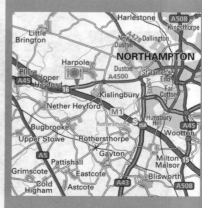

Red Lodge Transport Café

70 Turnpike Road, Old A11, Red Lodge, Nr Mildenhall IP28 8LB
Tel: 01638 750529

Directions: A11 from Newmarket to Thetford. Take exit B1085, between Junction 11 and division of A11 and A1065, to Red Lodge. This road runs parallel to A11. Red Lodge Transport Café is half way down on the east side, next to the Red Lion pub. Truck parking is on the opposite side of the road.

A long-established truckstop that has been under the same ownership for over 40 years and where nothing is too much trouble. Gerry Webster has seen much of life and is full of highly entertaining stories. The café has recently been re-decorated, but it is good to note that all the photographs of entertainment personalities who have eaten there on their travels have been put back in situ.

Set breakfast is well priced at £3.60. Gerry's most popular dish at the moment is a giant Yorkshire pudding with roast beef, two vegetables or beans, potatoes and gravy for £4.70. Also in demand are his daily roasts; shepherds pie; steak and kidney pudding, with potatoes and lots of fresh vegetables. The set dinner costs £3.80.

In the summer there are tables outside, either in front, or at the rear of the building in a small enclosed patio.

OPENING TIMES
Mon-Sun: 24 hours

FACILITIES
Disabled facilities
Newspapers
Parking: cars/trucks: plenty
Caravans/coaches welcome
Garden

FOOD AND DRINK
Seating: 60
Outdoor eating area
Daily specials
Kids' menu
Vegetarian menu
No alcoholic beverages

No credit cards

Robbo's Diner

A23 London Road, Pyecombe, Hurstpierpoint BN45 7FJ
Tel: 01273 844055

Directions: A23 south of Junction 11 and half a mile before A27,
Robbo's Diner is set back behind a lay-by. There is an old-style red telephone box
on entry to the car park.

Driving down to Brighton along the busy A23 you will find Robbo's Diner. It is on a fast stretch of the road - use the red BT telephone box, at the end of the lay-by as your marker. Named after its owner, Robbo (Chris Robinson), this café is well placed for the volume of traffic that uses this road to the south coast – a factor that can affect how busy the Diner becomes and the welcome you receive, as it is the only café on this stretch of road.

It is clean and functional with bright red seats and tabletops. The menu consists of generous portions of good everyday food made to order, with an all-day breakfast, burgers, fast foods, and a lunch and dinner menu.

OPENING TIMES

Mon-Fri:	05.45 - 15.00
Sat:	05.45 - 12.00 noon
Sun;	
Public holidays:	Closed

FACILITIES

Disabled facilities
Washroom for drivers
Newspapers
Parking: cars: 30; trucks: few in lay-by
Caravans/coaches welcome

FOOD AND DRINK

Seating: 48
Daily specials
Kids' menu
Vegetarian menu
No alcoholic beverages

No credit cards

The Rookery Café

A1000, North Mimms, Welham Green AL9 5SF
Tel: 07742 401223

Directions: On A1000 southbound from Hatfield, close to Junction 2 of A1(M).
Café is situated on west side of road. Easy to locate.

Although Lili the new proprietor has only been at The Rookery a short time, he has completely renovated and transformed the café. The exterior of the building has also been repainted and looks very welcoming with flowering hanging baskets along the front wall. The café is now light and airy with light blue walls and darker blue windows with shutters. Lili already has a group of regulars using the café enjoying the good, simple menu that he has created. Delicious looking food comes from the renovated kitchens. Top requests are for the breakfasts – half breakfasts at £3.50; full ones at £4.50, a large at £5.00. Also available are filled sandwiches like egg mayo at £1.50, black pudding and bacon at £2.35 and a top-of-the-range delicacy of smoked salmon with scrambled egg on toast at £3.75. More work is planned including an outside eating area and children's play area.

OPENING TIMES

Mon-Fri:	06.00 - 15.00
	17.00 - 20.00
Sat-Sun;	
Public holidays:	Closed

FACILITIES

Shower for drivers
Newspapers
Parking: car/trucks: plenty
Caravans/coaches welcome
Garden
Children's play area

FOOD AND DRINK

Seating: 40
Outdoor eating area
Daily specials
Kids' menu
Vegetarian menu
No alcoholic beverages

No credit cards

The Rose Café

London Road (A414), Widford, Chelmsford OM2 81G
Tel: 01245 496788

Directions: On the A414 heading south from Chelmsford, about a mile from the roundabout at the start of the dual carriageway. Southbound traffic only.

Originally a snack bar for local cyclists, The Rose Café is now a small truckstop/diner, owned by Robert Moss. It is reasonably priced and appears to have a strong local clientele as well as passers-by who come in for breakfasts and midday meals. Motorcyclists on 'rideouts' also drop in for something to eat.

The varied menu is all home cooked and baked. A selection from the menu would include variety of homemade pies, served with vegetables and mashed potato for £4.50; shepherds pie with vegetables £4.50; steak sandwich £3.50; steak, egg and chips £4.80. Desserts include jam roly-poly, spotted dick, syrup sponge served with custard or ice cream £1.50. Apple pie with custard or ice cream £1.70.

OPENING TIMES

Mon-Fri:	07.00 - 14.30
Sat-Sun:	07.00 - 13.00
Public holidays:	Closed

FACILITIES

Newspapers: read only
Parking: cars: 20; trucks: 10
Caravans/coaches welcome

FOOD AND DRINK

Seating: 40
Daily specials
Kids' menu
Vegetarian menu
No alcoholic beverages

No credit cards

Sarre Mill

Ramsgate Road, Sarre CT7 0JU

Tel: 01843 847573

Directions: Sarre Mill is at the junction of the A28 Canterbury/Margate road and the A253. The windmill stands on an exposed site at the western end of the Isle of Thanet. Easy to spot.

Sarre Mill is a "Smock" type windmill that was renovated in the 1980s. It's now in pristine condition and is one of only six working windmills in this country. It has seven floors, the bottom two of brick construction and five above of wooden frames and boards. About two tonnes of grain are milled a week and the resulting flour, muesli, and oats are sold in the adjacent shop, and in farm shops throughout Kent.

The café, which is of wood, lined with shelving, sells the stone ground flour, as well as bread, cakes, biscuits, special sauces, relishes etc. There is no 'specials' menu.

There is a shop selling antiques and they also sell plants.

Occasionally there are vintage car meetings or steam engine rallies here. The Mill is open to the public.

OPENING TIMES

April - Oct
Mon-Sun;
Public holidays: 10.00 - 17.00
Nov-March
Tue-Sun: 10.00 - 16.00

FACILITIES

Disabled facilities
Parking: cars: 20; trucks: no
Caravans/coaches welcome
Garden
Children's play area

FOOD AND DRINK

Seating: 45
Outdoor eating area
Daily specials; Kids' menu
Vegetarian menu
No alcoholic beverages

No credit cards

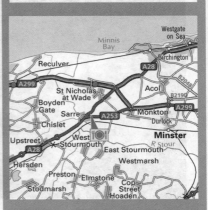

Scoffer's Café A45

Nene Valley Way Service Area, A45, Northampton NN3 5LU

Tel: 01602 784 500

Directions: Follow the A45 east along the Northampton ring road. After signs for Great Billing, look for sign for 24-hour filling station. There is eastbound access only.

Scoffer's Café has been operating from this site for five years and is popular with those who regularly travel the west–east route around Northampton. It's also handy for truckers as there is plenty of parking for large vehicles, and overnight parking is free. However, this café is only accessible to traffic travelling east.

Scoffer's, run by Mr Hilliard, has recently won an award for serving the best breakfast in Northamptonshire. What better recommendation can there be!

The specials include mixed grill and cottage pie. All the food is prepared and cooked to order on site, is well presented and always piping hot. Unusually, Scoffers also offers a menu for those on the Atkins Diet.

There is a 24-hour filling station on the same site and a shop selling daily papers and confectionery.

OPENING TIMES

Mon-Fri:	07.00 - 17.00
Sat-Sun:	
Public holidays:	07.00 - 18.00

FACILITIES

Disabled facilities
Newspapers: read only
Parking: cars: 30; trucks: 10
Security: overhead lighting
Caravans/coaches welcome
Children's play area

FOOD AND DRINK

Seating: 80
Outdoor eating area
Daily specials
Kids' menu
Vegetarian menu
Alcoholic beverages

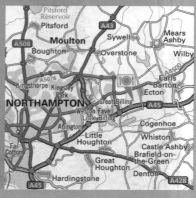

Silver Ball Transport Café

A10 London Road, Reed, Nr Royston ST8 8PD

Tel: 01763 848200

Directions: Situated on the A10, about three miles south of Royston and to the north of the village of Reed. The Café is on the west side of the road.

The Silver Ball Café is on the old Roman road joining the Great North Road with Ware in Hertfordshire. It's thought to have been a coaching inn originally, but became a garage and filling station and has been a well-known truckstop for over 60 years.

As the café is open at weekends it's a popular stopping place for walkers, cyclists and motorcyclists. Owner Tim Mustafa has shelves in one corner with a notice 'Crash Helmets Only'. The walls are hung with prints of old cars and bikes, and a noticeboard advertises bike parts for sale.

Special dish – roast pork, stuffing and vegetables.

OPENING TIMES

Mon-Fri: 06.30 - 22.00
Sat-Sun;
Public holidays: 08.00 - 16.00

FACILITIES

Washroom for drivers
Parking: cars: 20; trucks: 20, overnight charge possible
Security: yes
Caravans/coaches welcome
Garden

FOOD AND DRINK

Seating
Outdoor eating area
Daily specials
Kids' menu
Vegetarian menu
No alcoholic beverages

No credit cards

The Silver Bell Café and Diner

518 London Road, Ashford, Nr Hounslow TW15 3AE

Directions: Exit the M25 at Junction 13 and take the A30 eastbound to London. As The Silver Bell is on the south side of the dual carriageway, continue to the next roundabout and return on the A30 to reach the café.

Since opening in January 2005 this café has done very well. Manager Raynee welcomes everyone warmly and provides some of the best open bacon sandwiches around, with thick fresh crusty white bread and four great slices of bacon for £1.20 – fantastic. The special breakfast includes, 2 eggs, 2 bacon, 2 sausages, beans or tomatoes, chips or bubble and squeak, toast or bread, tea or coffee at a bargain £5.50.

The daily specials include steak, chips and peas for £4.50; salad of chicken, ham or cheese at £4.50 and also omelettes with different fillings starting at £2.00, and a selection of desserts. Monday to Friday there's a reduction for seniors of £1.00 off their meals.

On Saturday and Sundays, children having a meal with their family can have a free soda drink.

OPENING TIMES

Mon-Fri:	07.00 - 15.00
Sat:	08.00 - 14.00
Sun:	08.00 - 13.30
Public holidays:	Closed

FACILITIES

Disabled facilities
Newspapers
Parking: cars/trucks: plenty
Caravans/coaches welcome

FOOD AND DRINK

Seating: 35
Outdoor eating area
Daily specials
Kids' menu
Vegetarian menu
No alcoholic beverages

No credit cards

South Mimms Truckstop

Junction 23 M25/A1(M), South Mimms, Potters Bar EN6 3NE

Tel: 01707 649998

Directions: Follow A1000 and services sign. Located behind the Marriott Hotel at BP station. From the A1(M) and M25, exit at Junction 23 and follow 'Services' sign, the 'LGV' signs.

The South Mimms Truckstop is one of a series built specifically to provide a stopping place for BP truckers, but has now changed hands. Julia Sterritt, the manageress, finds running the establishment one of her most satisfying jobs, having also run fast food outlets. 'This is more fun' she says, as truckers are easy going with plenty of banter.

Samples of meals on the menu include roasts at £5.99; cottage pie £5.45 or sweet and sour chicken £4.90 and there is a selection of popular desserts like jam roly poly, all at £1.50. A mug of tea is 95p, with endless refills.

South Mimms has fast diesel pumps, a fully stocked truck shop, rest room and a dedicated area for gaming machines.

Truckers arrive around 17.00 for the night. For those who sleep in their cabs there is a public house within walking distance.

OPENING TIMES
Mon-Sun: 05.00 - 22.00
Public holidays: Closed

FACILITIES
Disabled facilities
Washroom for drivers
Newspapers
Cash machine
Parking: cars: 10; trucks: 174, parking £15.00; £4.00 meal; £2.00 shower
Security: CCTV, fenced
Diesel

FOOD AND DRINK
Seating: 98
Daily specials
Vegetarian menu
No alcoholic beverages

Square Deal Café

Bath Road, Knowl Hill, Reading RG10 9UR
Tel: 01628 822426

Directions: Leave M40 at Junction 4, or M4 Junction 8/9 for A404(M) – take A4 west. Square Deal is approximately three miles west, between Reading and Maidenhead. Café is set back on lay-by near the Seven Stars public house.

In the pretty village of Knowl Hill on the edge of the Chilterns is the unpretentious Square Deal Café. It's very popular with truckers because it serves just what they want – a square deal English breakfast, all day. At £5.20 it is good value for money with plates well filled with good fresh food.

Many tourists seem to find their way to the Square Deal as well, because it is exactly how you would imagine an English café should be. Evelyn, the manageress, always has a friendly smile and is clearly used to posing for photographs.

The café is clean and functional and the small team of staff are very friendly, welcoming both their regulars as well as new faces with the same enthusiasm.

There is plenty of space for parking in the enormous area at the back.

The café is closed at weekends.

OPENING TIMES
Mon-Fri: 06.00 - 14.30
Sat-Sun:
Public holidays: Closed

FACILITIES
Disabled facilities
Newspapers
Parking: cars: plenty; trucks: plenty, refrigerated spaces
Caravans welcome
Coaches: no

FOOD AND DRINK
Seating: 30
Kids' menu
Vegetarian menu
No alcoholic beverages

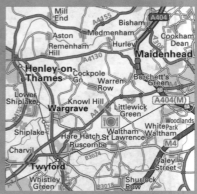

Stonar Café

Sandwich Industrial Estate, Ramsgate Road (A256), Sandwich CT13 9LY
Tel: 01304 612912

Directions: A256 between Ramsgate and Sandwich. At Sandwich, follow truck signs for Sandwich Industrial Estate, through a series of roundabouts. Stonar Café is at the entrance to the industrial estate on the left.

Stonar Café is easy to find. Originally, Stonar Café was the guardhouse at the entrance to Stonar airfield (the cell windows can be seen at the rear of the building). Stonar airfield was used during the Second World War by Coastal Command, serving as a 'diversion' airfield when others inland were fogbound, and vice versa. The meals here are the usual all-day breakfasts, as well as one or two specials such as shepherd's pie with vegetables and gravy, and steak and kidney pie with vegetables and gravy, or mixed cold meats with salad and chips.

Because Sandwich is one of the Cinque Ports and has Roman connections, the area is designated a special site of historic interest. There is a lake nearby with an old steam engine at the bottom, used by local sub-aqua divers.

OPENING TIMES

Mon-Fri:	07.30 - 14.00
Sat-Sun;	
Public holidays:	Closed

FACILITIES

Disabled facilities
Parking: cars: 10; trucks: 4
Caravans welcome
Coaches: no

FOOD AND DRINK

Seating:60
Daily specials
Kids' menu
Vegetarian menu
No alcoholic beverages

No credit cards

The Super Sausage Cafeteria

A5 Watling Street, Pottersbury, Towcester NN12 7QD
Tel: 01908 542964
Directions: A5 between Milton Keynes and A43 Northampton.
Super Sausage is situated at the north end of Pottersbury village.

Close to Towcester racecourse and Silverstone racetrack is the Super Sausage Cafeteria, owned by local firm It's a Gift Limited. The white single-storey building is easy to spot with its bright green and white-striped awnings.

The cafeteria has been going for over 22 years. It's clean and simple with a buzz to the atmosphere and a very good reputation. Pictures of racing drivers hang on the wall and the menu uses racing terms: beverages are 'Lubricants', breakfasts are 'Formula 1' at £3.25 or 'Formula 4' at £3.50, with 'accessories' (tomatoes, mushrooms etc). Fry-ups and omelettes are available and also a range of specials from baguettes to steaks to homemade cakes. Children's favourites on the menus come under the heading of 'Learners' – nuggets, fish fingers, etc.

Outside there is a tiny secluded garden, and in front of the café are plenty of trestle tables and chairs – popular with weekend bikers.

OPENING TIMES

Mon-Fri:	07.00 - 18.00
Sat-Sun:	08.00 - 16.00
Sun:	08.00 - 13.30
Public holidays:	08.00 - 14.00

FACILITIES

Newspapers
Parking: cars/trucks: plenty
Caravans/coaches welcome
Garden

FOOD AND DRINK

Seating: 60
Outdoor eating area
Daily specials
Kids' menu
Vegetarian menu
No alcoholic beverages

No credit cards

Truckworld Thurrock

Oliver Road, West Thurrock RM30 3ED

Tel:01708 860040   Fax: 01708 869130

Directions: Exit M25 at Junction 30. Follow the A13 for Southend, until the A126 junction. Follow the A126 through roundabouts. Look for Ikea, carry on down the road to the left and continue following 'Truck' signs. Truckworld is on the right.

Truckworld Thurrock is not to be confused with Thurrock Services. Built specifically for lorry transporters, it was constructed about 15 years ago and has, in the last three years, been refurbished.

There is space for about 50 cars to park and ample parking for 250 trucks. Diesel fuel is on the site and there is a truck wash. The whole compound is fenced, with overnight security patrols.

The building has about 65 letting rooms (single and twin only, mainly for contractors), available either on a weekly or monthly basis. There is a fully licensed bar, truckers' shop, pool table and TV. On four nights of the week, adult entertainment is laid on for residents.

Outside there is a pleasant small garden with a barbeque and inside, a truckers' shower area. In addition to their work at Truckworld, owners Nick Ashby and Andrew Wilson are both active and keen contributors to charities.

OPENING TIMES

Mon-Sun:	24 hours
Public holidays:	Closed

(open for rooms and truck parking)

FACILITIES

Disabled facilities
Washroom for drivers; Newspapers
Parking: cars: 50; trucks: 250,
overnight £12.00 inc. £3.00 meal
voucher. Diesel fuel and truck wash
Security: lighting/patrolled/
CCTV/fenced; Caravans/coaches
welcome; Garden

ACCOMMODATION

Twin: economy: £15.00 (p.p.)
Twin: large £16.50 (p.p.)
Single: ensuite; TV: £22.00

FOOD AND DRINK

Seating: 100
Outdoor eating area
Daily specials; Kids' menu
Vegetarian menu
Alcoholic beverages (evenings)

Tudor Café at Luton Truckstop

Chaul End Lane, Luton LU4 8EZ
Tel: 01582 597637 Ext 3

Directions: Exit the M1 at Junction 11 and head along the A505 towards Luton. Pass through several sets of traffic lights and turn right at the roundabout. The café is about a quarter of a mile down a slip road.

The Luton Truckstop is on a three-acre site in an industrial area of Luton.

It is run by Les Allen who has built up this business over a number of years. Also in this compound he has a truck repair shop. There are a number of single and twin rooms to let, all with their own wash-basin, toilet and TV. The café has a bright and airy atmosphere and serves a wide variety of food. There is also a large bar, with a pool table and a function room that can be used for private parties. The chalked up specials on the board might include

lamb shank for £5.50 or breaded fish and chips for £3.95 – all with veg. Desserts include rice pudding, treacle sponge and peaches and ice cream all under £1.30.

The truckstop may relocate sometime in the near future, so it's advisable to phone in advance.

OPENING TIMES
Mon-Fri: 06.00 - 21.30
Sun:
Public holidays: 07.00 - 14.30

FACILITIES
Disabled facilities
Washroom for drivers
Newspapers
Cash machine
Parking: cars: 50; trucks: 50, overnight £5.00, refrigerated
Caravans welcome

ACCOMMODATION
1 Double; 1 Single; 1 Family: £10.00 (p.p.)

FOOD AND DRINK
Seating: 80
Daily specials; Kids' menu
Vegetarian menu
Alcoholic beverages
No credit cards

Watling Street Café

A5/M1, London Road, Flamstead, Harpenden AL3 8HA

Tel: 01582 840270

Directions: Leave the M1 at Junction 9 and head northwest on the A5. The truckstop will be seen about half a mile up the road on the right hand side at Flamstead, behind the filling station.

The café is not particularly easy to spot, as the CDC truckshop is right in front of the building. With amenities for truck drivers, it is very definitely aimed at those drivers who wish to use it as a regular stopping point. There is overnight parking for trucks, a cash machine is available in the filling station shop and there is a public phone box on the site.

The smartly presented diner, run by Jane Wynne, has a TV and provides newspapers to read. There is an long list of daily special meals including roast chicken, steak and kidney pie and chicken pie, all with the usual vegetables, gravy, chips or mashed potatoes for £4.30 which is very good value. For dessert the choice includes lemon sponge, apple pie, chocolate chip sponge and lemon meringue pie, all priced at £1.80.

OPENING TIMES

Mon-Thu:	06.00 - 21.30
Fri:	06.00 - 17.30
Sat:	07.00 - 12.45
Sun; Public holidays:	Closed

FACILITIES

Washroom for drivers
Newspapers
Cash machine in garage
Parking: cars: 25; trucks: 80
Security: CCTV; lit perimeter
Caravans/coaches welcome

FOOD AND DRINK

Seating: 60
Daily specials
Kids' menu
Vegetarian menu
No alcoholic beverages

No credit cards

North Wales, the Midlands and the North

This region includes the following counties:

Cambridgeshire (part)
Cheshire
Cumbria Part of
Derbyshire
Greater Manchester
Isle of Man
Lancashire
Leicestershire
Lincolnshire
Merseyside

Norfolk
Northamptonshire (part)
Nottinghamshire
Rutland
Shropshire (part)
Staffordshire
Warwickshire (part)
West Midlands
Yorkshire, East Riding of

Yorkshire, North (part)
Yorkshire, South
Yorkshire, West
Anglesey
Conwy
Denbighshire
Flintshire
Gwynedd
Powys (part)
Wrexham

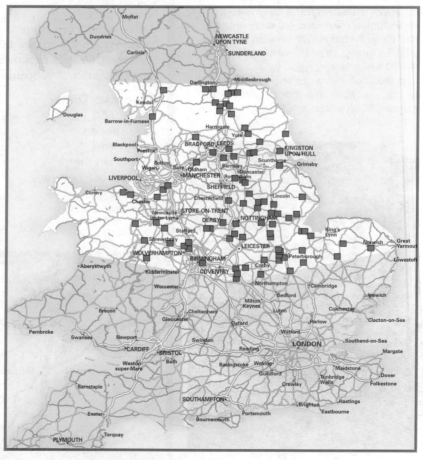

INDEX
North Wales, the Midlands and the North

A1 Truckstop Diner

A151 Bourne Road, Colsterworth NG33 5JN
Tel: 01476 860916

Directions: On the A1 between Peterborough and grantham at Colsterworth roundabout. Take the A151 to Bourne off the roundabout. The A1 Truckstop Diner is about 200 yards along the A151 on the right-hand side.

Easy to spot with its bright silver cladding and bright red signage, the Portakabin that is the A1 Truckstop Diner is in a prime position alongside the A151 to Bourne. A true truckstop with truckers' ambiance and camaraderie, it has a ticket numbering ordering system. Customers can choose from freshly prepared food such as all-day breakfasts at £3.85 including tea re-fills and more toast; or scampi or ham salads with chips or potatoes – £4.50 (huge!) and a selection of filled jacket potatoes or perhaps pork chops with veg for £4.35. In the evening you might find locally produced lamb shank for £4.55, or steak and kidney pudding. Bottled beer is available.

In spite of the fast turn around, there's still time for diners to have another mug of tea and catch up with each other.

On site is a fully serviced truckstop with gas, diesel, and a CDC truck shop.

OPENING TIMES
Mon-Fri: 06.00 - 21.00
Sat: 06.00 - 12.00
Sun; Public holidays: Closed

FACILITIES
Disabled facilities – wheelchair access; Washroom for drivers
Newspapers.
Parking: cars: plenty; trucks: 60, refrigerated spaces
Security: lighting, 24-hour patrol, fenced
Caravans/coaches welcome

FOOD AND DRINK
Seating: 76
Daily specials; Kids' menu
Vegetarian menu
Alcoholic beverages: beer only

No credit cards

Abbey Parks Farm Café

A17 Abbey Parks Farm Shop, East Heckington, Boston PE20 3QG

Tel: 01205 821610

Directions: On fast A17 between Sleaford and Boston, approximately seven miles from Sleaford, in East Heckington. Entrance shared with BP petrol station on south side of road. Approach with care. There is signage.

A farm shop, restaurant and café with very high standards, decorated with interesting farming, gardening and kitchen memorabilia. Meals are prepared fresh every day, sourced where possible from the owner's farm and local growers – the farm is renowned for its asparagus.

Homemade soups – courgette, tomato and herb soup; butternut squash and red pepper to name a few are at £2.75. Main courses include stuffed marrow, haddock kedgeree, a full variety of local sausages and bacon, and of course the Sunday roast of lamb, beef or pork at £7.95 – popular so it's advisable to book. Puddings also are made daily using local fresh fruits. Breakfasts are available all day, a full breakfast costs £4.25, and light tasties from £3.25. Seniors get a 10% discount on Tuesdays.

The farm shop sells local cheeses, jams and preserves, fresh fruit and vegetables and plants.

Outside is very attractive closed patio area.

OPENING TIMES
Mon-Sat: 08.30 - 17.30
Sun;
Public holidays: 09.30 - 17.00

FACILITIES
Disabled facilities
Newspapers; Cash back
Parking: cars: 25; trucks: nearby
Caravans: welcome
Coaches: advance notice required
Garden
Children's play area

FOOD AND DRINK
Seating: 80
Outdoor eating area
Kids' menu
Vegetarian menu
Alcoholic beverages

The Anglia Motel

A17, Fleet Hargate, Holbeach PO12 8LT

Tel: 01406 422766

Directions: The Anglia Motel is on the south side of the A17 at Fleet Hargate, heading east from Holbeach to King's Lynn.

A Hawker Hunter jet, lovingly restored by the local air cadets, stands in the forecourt of this motel, a popular stopping place for coaches, especially during the tulip season, and also for those travelling to the east coast. Currently being modernised, the motel has a reception area with a pool table and large armchairs and a separate eating area – basic but adequate. On one wall is memorabilia of the Fen people's participation during World War II, from the veterans of Arnhem to the local airborne division. There are poignant letters, newspaper cuttings, war citations and photographs providing a moving historical insight into the wartime period.

Owner Harold Payne ensures the cafeteria supplies good, basic home cooking and generous portions – full English breakfast is £4.50; roast beef with Yorkshire pudding and seasonal vegetables £4.75; vegetarian lasagne £4.95, or gammon at £6.25 (both including chips, peas and optional extras).

OPENING TIMES
Mon-Sun;
Public holidays: 07.00 - 21.00

FACILITIES
Disabled facilities
Washroom for drivers
Newspapers
Parking: cars: 60; trucks: 100, refrigerated spaces
Security: yes
Caravans/coaches welcome
Garden

ACCOMMODATION
10 Doubles + single bed; TV:
£34.50 a room

FOOD AND DRINK
Seating: 100
Outdoor eating area
Daily specials; Kids' menu
Vegetarian menu
Alcoholic beverages

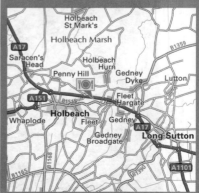

Barney's

WND Catering Ltd, Melton Road, Barnetby Top DN38 6LU
Tel: 01652 680966

Directions: Take exit 5 off the M180/A15/A18 towards Humberside Airport and follow the signs for the Airport and Grimsby. Barney's is set back off the road with a large car/truck park in front of the property and surrounded by open countryside.

Wendy Nundy, Barneys' new proprietor has totally refurbished and redecorated the café since returning to her hometown after two years living in France. She is determined to make Barney's a locally well-known name for good food and good hospitality. The building offers two very different eating options: the ground floor all-day café, and upstairs restaurant called Café de Chauffeur. Wendy has also installed air conditioning.

Breakfasts are an important feature on the menu as are Wendy's daily specials that include steak and ale pie (£4.95); chicken Kiev (£4.75); and fish pie (£4.75) all served with chips or potatoes and vegetables.

Upstairs in the Café de Chauffeur, Wendy has created a totally different style. It has its own entrance with an intimate bar and comfortable leather sofa and restaurant menu that will include a fish dishes and speciality dishes using local meats and vegetables.

Opening Times

Mon-Fri:	06.00 - 21.00
Sat:	06.00 - 14.00
Sun:	09.00 - 18.00
Public holidays:	07.00 - 18.00

Facilities

Disabled facilities
Washroom for drivers
Newspapers
Parking: cars: plenty; trucks: plenty, refrigerated spaces
Caravans/coaches welcome

Food and Drink

Seating: 40
Outdoor eating area
Daily specials
Kids' menu
Vegetarian menu
Alcoholic beverages

No Credit cards: available soon

Beechwood Café

Market Weighton Road, Holme upon Spalding Moor, York YO43 4ED
Tel: 01430 860453

Directions: A 614 between Goole and Market Weighton, Holme upon Spalding Moor is two miles south of Market Weighton. Set well outside the village., it is well signposted.

Once a nightclub, it would have received no complaints about noise as it is some way outside the village. Today it is a secure truck park, together with a very pleasant, well-established café. Owners Mr and Mrs Goldsmith have been here over 23 years. Popular with locals as well as truck drivers and tourists, Beechwood has a large menu including daily specials. Breakfasts are served until 11.30 each day – prices starting at £4.00. Battered haddock, chips, peas, tea, bread and butter, £4.75; Newport steak pie, chips, peas and gravy, £4.75; 10oz (283g) gammon steak, chip and peas, £5.25. Also available – vegetarian meals and a children's menu board with familiar fish fingers, or chicken teddies around £2.50. There are high chairs, and staff will heat up baby's milk and food.

In the summer the outside tables and colourful flowering baskets help make the café a popular meeting place for motorcyclists as well.

OPENING TIMES
Mon-Sun: 07.00 - 18.00
Public holidays: 07.00 - 18.00

FACILITIES
Newspapers
Parking: cars/trucks: plenty
Caravans/coaches welcome

FOOD AND DRINK
Seating: 100
Outdoor eating area
Daily specials
Kids' menu
Vegetarian menu
No alcoholic beverages

No credit cards

Big Al's Diner

A17 Newark Road, North Rauceby, Sleaford NG34 8ET

Tel: 01529 488491

Directions: On A17 Sleaford to Newark road on north side next to Jet petrol station and Cheerio's Truckstop (one mile from A15/A17 roundabout).

Owner Kim Harrison opened the doors to Big Al's Diner in May of 2004. Her enthusiasm and welcome are charming and her effective, simple decorative flair has made Big Al's a great success. Her attention to detail shines through from her extensive well-produced and well-thought out menu to her desire to re-introduce good, old-fashioned, long forgotten English foods. Rice puddings and semolinas, proper locally produced sausages and freshly mashed potatoes are proving to be extremely popular with customers. Her motto ' Your satisfaction is our pleasure' runs very true. The influence of nearby R.A.F. Cranwell is evident in the signed prints of airforce planes hanging on the walls, which we understand are for sale.

Refurbishment is on going and Kim hopes to have the garden area ready next. From January 2006, the restaurant will be no smoking.

OPENING TIMES
Mon-Fri;
Public Holiday: 07.00 - 19.30

FACILITIES
Disabled facilities
Newspapers
Parking: cars: 30; trucks: at
Cheerio's next-door
Caravans/coaches welcome

FOOD AND DRINK
Seating: 50
Outdoor eating area
Daily specials
Kids' menu
Vegetarian menu
Alcoholic beverages

Billy Jean's Café

Unit 2, Haven Garage, The Nant, Pentre Halkyn, Holywell CH8 8BD
Tel: 01352 781118
Directions: Just off Junction 32A, between A5026 and A55.

New owners of the café, Mr N and Mr P Parry, are totally refurbishing and extending the café to seat 70 people. The rooms have been opened up into one large space on slightly different levels, which makes the whole area interesting, decorated in light colours and pinewood finishes. Outside, the cream exterior is awaiting new signage.

A varied menu and the plates of hot food coming out from the kitchen are what make it is so popular: roast ham, mushroom and peas, £3.70; lamb stew at £3.40 and roast beef with 2 vegetables at £3.50. A jumbo breakfast will cost £4.00 with a second cup of tea free with every meal. Coffee 10p extra.

The café was named after the tennis star Billy Jean King by the previous owner who was a fan of hers. There are framed pictures and tributes to her success hung on the café walls.

OPENING TIMES

Mon-Thu:	07.30 - 15.30
Fri:	07.30 - 15.30
Sat:	07.30 - 12.00
Sun:	
Public holidays:	Closed

FACILITIES

Disabled facilities
Newspapers
Parking: cars/trucks: plenty
Caravans welcome
Coaches: no

FOOD AND DRINK

Seating: 60
Daily specials
Kids' menu
Vegetarian menu
No alcoholic beverages

No credit cards

Birch Lea Café

A46 Newark Road, Swinderby, Lincoln LN6 9HN
Tel: 01522 869293

Directions: A46 travelling east from Newark to Lincoln, about half way between the two. The café is set back off the road, near Swinderby.

This is a SAT NAV designated lorry park, and is also a rather good café, popular with the coach companies as one of their favourite and regular stopping places for a break for snacks and interesting meals. The very full breakfasts start at £5.00 and include all the trimmings, with a smaller version for £3.10. A comprehensive menu includes daily specials, vegetarian meals and kids foods.

The café is prettily decorated in chalet style with wooden tables and chairs and hanging lamps. Plates on a picture rail decorate the large room, and framed beer mats from the different breweries hang on the walls.

There is a large cold drink fridge, CDs for sale and a pinball football game, snooker table and high chairs – it is a café that offers something for everyone.

They are happy to prepare takeaway food and to make deliveries.

OPENING TIMES

Mon-Fri:	07.00 - 15.00
Sat:	08.00 - 15.00
Sun;	
Public holidays:	08.00 - 14.00

FACILITIES

Washroom for drivers
Newspapers
Parking: cars/trucks: plenty
Caravans/coaches welcome

FOOD AND DRINK

Seating: 52
Outdoor eating area
Kids' menu
Vegetarian menu
No alcoholic beverages

No credit cards

Birmingham Truckstop

The Wharf, Wharf Road, Tyseley, Birmingham B11 2EB
Tel: 0121 628 2339   Fax 0121 628 2364

Directions: A45 into Birmingham – then signs for Tyseley Industrial Estate, following 'Truck' signs. Situated on the wharf on Wharf Road.

The Birmingham Truckstop is dedicated to the comfort and entertainment of the long-distance lorry driver. Run by Leo McGroaty. it is an efficient, no-frills establishment that seeks to fulfil the needs of the tired traveller. The fully equipped bar and cafeteria have big-screen televisions showing Sky sports. There is plenty of accommodation, or cab sleepers can pay is £5 per night, which includes a free sauna. Trucks can be left safely as the fenced compound is locked at 18:00 every evening. Late arrivals can, however, gain entry as the area is patrolled at night. The cafeteria is open from 06:00 to 21:00 and the bar from 12.00 noon until 23:00.There is an extensive menu that includes a steak breakfast at £3.50 and a selection of dinners from £2.85. Specials include traditional roasts with all the trimmings at £3.40.

OPENING TIMES
Mon-Sun:
Public holidays: 06.00 - 21.00

FACILITIES
Parking: cars: 120; trucks: 30
Security: CCTV, fencing
(gates locked 18.00 but
admission at any time)
Caravans/coaches welcome

ACCOMMODATION
8 Twins; 32 Singles:
ensuite; TV: £20.00 (p.p)
inc. breakfast

FOOD AND DRINK
Seating: not given
Daily specials
Alcoholic beverages

No credit cards

Bistro Café

A52 Nottingham Road, Sedgebrooke, Grantham NG32 8EP

Tel: 01949 842 164

Directions: The Bistro Café is found two and a half miles east of the A1 at Grantham, along the A52 Nottingham road, from the A1. Next to the Barrowby Garage, which specialises in used Land Rovers and military vehicles, the café is easy to spot.

Jude Maples took over the Bistro Café two years ago and it is obvious that all the hard work and long hours she has put in are really paying off. You can tell she loves the job and has established a good repartee with her regular customers, but everyone receives a genuine welcome.

It is counter service only, providing workmen's breakfasts and a daily selection of basic but hearty meals from a selection of homemade pies, fresh lasagne and lots of fresh vegetables, all of the highest quality and served with a smile.

The Bistro Café is open for one hour longer in the summer to enable passers by to sit at the large café windows and enjoy the stunningly beautiful views of Belvoir Castle set up on the hill, and the surrounding Lincolnshire countryside.

OPENING TIMES
Mon-Fri: 07.00 - 16.00
Sat: 07.00 - 14.00
Sun;
Public holidays: 08.00 - 14.00

FACILITIES
Newspapers
Parking: cars: 15; trucks: 5
Security: patrolled
Caravans/coaches welcome

FOOD AND DRINK
Seating: 44
Daily specials
Kids' menu
Vegetarian menu
No alcoholic beverages

No credit cards

BJ's Transport Café

Sudbury Services, Lichfield Road, Sudbury DE6 5GX
Tel: 01283 820669

Directions: On the A515, two miles south of Sudbury on the Lichfield road.

BJ's is an old transport café and garage, the building dating from the 1930s in a mock Art Deco style. Keith and Linda re-opened the café four years ago and now have a dedicated customer base, loyal enough to divert miles to eat here.

Daily specials include sweet and sour chicken; quiche and salad and roast beef with all the trimmings, and for dessert, spotted dick, apple crumble and cheesecake.

At the rear of the building there is a truck shop supplying truckers' daily requirements and other items such as portable TVs, tin kettles, rugs, spotlights etc. Newspapers can be obtained from the adjacent filling station where there is also a cash machine.

OPENING TIMES

Mon-Thu:	07.00 - 22.00
Fri:	07.00 - 20.00
Sat-Sun:	
Public holidays:	Closed

FACILITIES

Washroom for drivers
Newspapers & cash machine at adjacent filling station
Parking: cars: 8; trucks: 25
Security: lighting
Caravans/coaches: no

FOOD AND DRINK

Seating: 34
Outdoor eating area
Daily specials
Kids' menu
Vegetarian menu
No alcoholic beverages

No credit cards

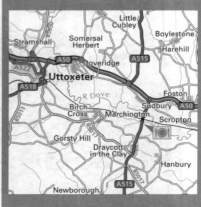

Burnzies Café

10 Skipton Road, Steeton, Keighley BD20 6TA
Tel: 01535 656120

Directions: From Skipton to Keighley on the A629, take B6265 into Steeton. Up High Street and at crossroads adjacent to Goats Head pub, turn right and Burnzies Café is almost immediately on the left. Signage on road at entrance to café.

The Burnzies Café looks like a family house, and stands opposite the public gardens and park.

Inside the house, attractively decorated with warm red walls and with large Georgian sash windows that open out onto a grassy bank, you are made to feel very welcome by the friendly catering team.

Jacqueline, who was holding the fort for owner Pat Burns and cooking that day, told me that the food is all prepared in-house daily and is homemade. The truckers 'Belt Buster' breakfast at £3.60 with toast, tea, black pudding, bacon, eggs, fried slice, potatoes and sauce is a serious undertaking. The special omelette dishes with a variety of different fillings are from around the £3.00. Steak and kidney pie, or cheese and onion pie with three accompanying vegetables, gravy and a pot of tea costs £3.30. Puddings like chocolate cake and fruit pies are from £1.00.

OPENING TIMES
Mon-Fri: 07.00 - 15.00
Sat: 08.00 - 12.00
Sun;
Public holidays: 07.00 - 15.00

FACILITIES
Washroom for drivers
Newspapers
Parking: cars/trucks: plenty
Caravans/coaches welcome

FOOD AND DRINK
Seating: 70
Daily specials
Vegetarian menu
No alcoholic beverages

No credit cards

Byard's Leap Country Kitchen

A17, Byard's Leap, Cranwell, Sleaford NG34 8EY
Tel: 01400 261375

Directions: Travelling in either direction between Newark and Sleaford on A17, look for the junction of the B6403 Ancaster Road. The café is in a dip behind trees on the right.

Byard's Leap Country Kitchen has been here for at least eighty years, some of the wooden extensions having been constructed from disused billet huts from nearby R.A.F Cranwell. Cranwell cadets used to cycle here for decent food.

Named after the Legend of Byard's Leap, (Byard being a horse who, with local witch Meg, perished in a fire), the café is now run by Mr & Mrs Ewing who, at the time of writing, were constructing six ensuite bedrooms (one for disabled customers) and hope to have them ready by autumn 2005.

Byard's Leap specials include steak pie with vegetables at £4.75; liver, bacon and sausage with vegetables at £3.95 or ham egg and chips at £4.75. For dessert: treacle sponge, lemon sponge and crumbles served with custard or ice cream, all priced at £2.25

Close by there is a garage. Also, a 'Bubble Car' museum, open at weekends.

OPENING TIMES
Mon-Fri:	08.00 - 17.00
Sat:	07.00 - 17.00
Sun:	
Public holidays:	08.30 - 16.00
Xmas & New Year:	Closed

FACILITIES
Disabled facilities
Washroom for drivers
Newspapers: to read
Parking: cars: 50; trucks: limited
Security: garage lighting
Caravans/coaches welcome
Garden; Children's play area

ACCOMMODATION
Check availability

FOOD AND DRINK
Seating: 46
Outdoor eating area
Daily specials; Kids' menu
Vegetarian menu
Alcoholic beverages

Bypass Café

Cromwell Halt, Newark NG23 6JF
Tel: 07745 592170

Directions: For access northbound on the A1. Turn off A1 at signpost for Cromwell Halt and Doll Museum, and go into village. Turn right over A1 and left at mini roundabout up to café. The café has a bright red tiled roof with the word "café" tiled into it. For southbound, look for sign after Carlton on Trent for Cromwell Halt. The café is well signposted from the A1.

Celebrating 75 years as a roadside café the Bypass Café has a charm of its own. From the outside it looks like an attractive oversized wooden chalet.

Mr Hopkins has been the proprietor for about two years and his cooking is well known: home cooked ham, locally supplied vegetables and fresh meats, sandwiches, sweet and savoury pies are all so popular that the café is often quite full. One couple I met make a detour twice every week to arrive in time for breakfast at the café, and return for their evening meal.

Breakfasts with tea or coffee start at £3.95; roast meats or braised steaks meals with two vegetables, potatoes, bread and butter and a hot drink will cost £3.95; the mixed grill with add-ons is priced at £5.50.

Upgrades to the building are in progress and a new parking area has been laid.

OPENING TIMES
Mon-Fri:	06.00 - 20.00
Sat:	07.00 - 13.00
Sun;	
Public holidays:	Closed

FACILITIES
Washroom for drivers (shower: £2.00)
Newspapers
Parking: car/trucks: plenty
Caravans/coaches welcome
Garden

FOOD AND DRINK
Seating: 36
Outdoor eating area
Daily specials; Kids' menu
Vegetarian menu
No alcoholic beverages

No credit cards
Euros accepted

Café A19

A19 Services, Elwick, Hartlepool TS27 3HH

Tel: 01740 644223

Directions: Northbound on the A19 between Stockton-on-Tees and Sunderland, two miles after the A689 junction. A19 Café is situated in the Total filling station. Parking is at the rear, where there is another entrance to the café.

Supervisor, Andrea Murphy, was having a bad day when I arrived – they had been without electric power all day. However, she and her team were very welcoming and took me through their menu.

The café, always busy as a food stop on this busy stretch of road, offers a 'Bake and Bite' service: takeaway options such as sandwiches, wraps and rolls filled with a wide choice of fillings. On Fridays they have a special of hake fillet and chips for £2.50. There is also a special kids' menu of a sausage roll, doughnut or gingerbread man, crisps and a drink all for £1.89.

An area for smokers has been set aside, separate from the main restaurant. Accommodation is planned from 2006 so it is advisable check availability in advance Alongside the café is a shop selling bottled drinks, fast foods, ice creams and car accessories.

OPENING TIMES
Mon-Fri: 06.30 - 18.30
Sat-Sun:
Public holidays: 08.00 - 16.00

FACILITIES
Disabled facilities
Washroom for drivers
Newspapers
Parking: cars/trucks: plenty
Caravans/coaches welcome

FOOD AND DRINK
Seating: 60
Outdoor eating area
Daily specials
Kids' menu
Vegetarian menu
No alcoholic beverages

Cheerio's

A17 Newark Road, North Raucby, Sleaford NG34 8ET
Tel: 01529 488123

Directions: Heading east on the A17, just after the sign for the B1429, Cheerio's is two and a half miles further on, on the left. There is a filling station nearby. Heading west from Sleaford, Cheerio's is two miles out, just beyond the filling station and Big Al's Diner on the right.

Cheerio's has been established for many years. A photograph of the café shows that little has changed since the 1960s, except for food regulations. Eggs now have to be stamped with the EU mark, thus eliminating use of free-range eggs.

All the food is prepared in owner Stuart Hillson's home nearby, and is then cooked on the premises. Daily specials depend on the meat joints Stuart has prepared, so they would be based on beef, one day, chilli another and so on. A breakfast costs £3.90 and a cup of tea 50p. Also available, a range of delicious looking freshly baked pastries at £2.00 served with custard or ice cream.

While he is bringing up a young family Stuart has to close on a Sunday to allow himself time for them, but in meantime, he is planning some improvements

OPENING TIMES
Mon-Fri:	06.00 - 20.00
Sat:	06.00 - 14.00
Sun; Public holidays:	Closed

FACILITIES
Disabled facilities
Washroom for drivers
Newspapers
Parking: cars: 40; trucks: 20
Security: lighting
Caravans/coaches welcome

FOOD AND DRINK
Seating: 60
Daily specials (occasionally)
Kids' menu
Vegetarian menu
No alcoholic beverages

No credit cards

Christine's Diner

Boothferry Road, Boothferry Bridge, Howden, Goole DN14 7EF

Tel: 01430 430409

Directions: From M62, Junction 37 Howden exit, take A614 in the direction of Boothferry. Further along this road is the Ferryboat Inn and immediately opposite is Christine's Diner.

The café, with a view onto the Humber Bridge flyover, is a short drive from the busy port of Goole, so drivers are often talking about their latest trip overseas, or ship or port-related news.

Christine recently acquired the Diner and is slowly redecorating and modernising it, and also the external signage.

For those in a hurry, sandwiches can be pre-ordered in advance over the telephone and will be ready and waiting for you on arrival. As Christine is carrying out refurbishments it is best to call in advance to find out about price and availability of accommodation (normally for 150 people). A quiet, relaxing reception and lounge area has comfy chairs and TV. A pool table is in a separate room.

The area in front of the café is regularly used by Hopauctions (Hopkinsons Fairdeals own the land) to store equipment for viewing prior to their auctions, so it is very busy on those days.

OPENING TIMES

Mon-Thu:	05.30 - 22.00
Fri:	05.30 - 20.00
Sat:	07.00 - 15.00
Sun;	
Public holidays:	Closed

FACILITIES

Disabled facilities
Newspapers
Parking: cars: plenty; trucks: plenty, refrigerated spaces
Caravans/coaches welcome
Garden

ACCOMMODATION

Ring for information

FOOD AND DRINK

Seating: 150
Outdoor eating area
Daily specials; Kids' menu
Vegetarian menu
Alcoholic beverages

Clifton Bridge Café

Clifton Lane, Wilford NG11 7ES
Tel: 0115 9811467

Directions: From Junction 24 of the M1, take the A453 to Nottingham. Take the turning to Clifton village after about six and a half miles. The café is on the right with BP filling station adjacent.

Despite many road alterations, flyovers and the building of dual carriageways, the café remains much the same as it was many years ago, although it is not the original café.

In the 1940s Mrs Moran's grandfather had a smallholding across the road from this site. To supplement his agricultural living, the family opened a small snack shop for picnickers and this shop began to be frequented by the local lorry drivers, transporting gravel. As the lorry drivers began requesting meals, so the truckstop/café was born.

After compulsory purchase, the Morans built a house across the road, taking their customers with them and creating a lorry park, which is used much as it always has been, without any alterations.

The food is standard truckstop fare, as one would expect. There are no specials on offer, but delicious home-baked cakes. Mrs Moran also makes wedding cakes to order.

OPENING TIMES
Mon-Fri:	07.00 - 14.00
Sat:	07.00 - 12.00
Sun:	
Public holidays:	Closed

FACILITIES
Newspapers: read only
Parking: cars: 30; trucks: 15, overnight £4.50
Security: lighting
Caravans/coaches welcome

FOOD AND DRINK
Seating: 35
Kids' menu
Vegetarian menu
No alcoholic beverages

No credit cards

The Corner Cupboard

Birdforth, Easingwold, YO61 4NW

Tel: 01845 501495

Directions: On the A19 south of Thirsk – set back from the lay-by near the village of Birdforth.

A pretty, converted schoolhouse, built in the 1980s that has been tastefully restored and consists of a series of interconnecting rooms full of beautiful furniture. These rooms lead through to a conservatory dining area that is light and attractively styled.

Peter and Gerd Handley, owners since March 2004, have put their own mark on the premises. Gerd, from Scandinavia, looks after the interior design and gifts, shopping around Europe. Peter is the restaurateur and has devised a varied and enticing menu. Choices include twice-baked cheese soufflé; trio homemade pâté and main courses like chicken, mushroom and bacon pie, or pan-fried sea bass at £5.95. There are wonderful homemade cakes and pastries from £1.75 and a good selection of fresh coffees and teas.

The Corner Cupboard is very busy over weekends, as word has spread that it is a great shopping experience as well as a wonderful eating venue – so it's wise to book.

OPENING TIMES

Tue-Sat:	09.30 - 17.00
Mon; Sun:	Closed
Public holidays:	Closed

FACILITIES

Disabled facilities
Newspapers
Parking: cars: plenty: trucks: no
Caravans: no
Coaches: advance notice required
Garden

FOOD AND DRINK

Seating: 50
Daily specials
Kids' menu
Vegetarian menu
Alcoholic beverages

Dinky's Dinah

A458 Welshpool Road, Ford, Nr Shrewsbury SY5 9LG
Tel/Fax: 01743 850070

Directions: Take the road from Shrewsbury to Welshpool (A458). At the west end of the village of Ford, just after the Shrewsbury/Oswestry roundabout, Dinky's Dinah can be found in a lay-by on the right-hand side of the road.

Dinky's Dinah has been established for about fifteen years and is, we are told, one of three establishments of that name in the area. There is a seating area for up to eight people inside the cabin (most of it is taken up by the kitchen), but there is a covered outside seating area that is quite attractive, though basic. This will seat 24-26 people of a hardier nature! There is plenty of parking in the lay-by. Mr Dawes has a popular café (owned by Mrs Dawes) perhaps indicated by the 700 tea mugs he has to replace in a year! There are no daily specials but the usual truckstop fare is available.

There are regular meetings of local motorcycle clubs and there's a notice board that advertises motorcycle suits and spare parts, as well as other sundry notices.

OPENING TIMES
Mon-Sun;
Public holidays: 24 hours
Xmas Day; Boxing Day;
New Year's Day: Closed

FACILITIES
Disabled facilities
Newspapers
Parking: cars/trucks: in lay-by
Caravans/coaches welcome

FOOD AND DRINK
Seating: 8
Outdoor eating area
Kids' menu
Vegetarian menu
No alcoholic beverages

No credit cards

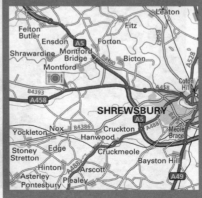

Dragon's Rest Café

St Asaph Road, Nr Lloc, North Wales CH8 8RF
Tel: 01352 720920

Directions: Along the north Welsh coast on A55, off Junction 31, just before the B5122. Well signposted and easy to locate, with plenty of parking

Once a derelict farmhouse, this building has been totally refurbished by the owners John and Debbie Davies who have created a very comfortable, and already popular café built of local Welsh stone with grey slate roof and set off by its new driveway entrance.

The staff gave me a very warm welcome into rooms decorated in a Welsh country style, (you'll see Welsh red dragons everywhere in all shapes and sizes) and old photographs of the surrounding area.

The ground floor café seat 28, while up an open staircase is another more comfortable and formal dining room seating 32 people. This is a non-smoking area.

Items on the menus range from a daily breakfast menu to a selection of dinners. Included were a variety of hot roasts starting at £5.50, plus a selection of hot puddings starting at £2.20 – all using local Welsh eggs, cheese, meats and vegetables.

OPENING TIMES
Mon-Sun;
Public holidays: 07.30 - 16.30

FACILITIES
Disabled facilities
Newspapers
Parking: cars: plenty; trucks: no
Caravans welcome
Coaches: advance notice required

FOOD AND DRINK
Seating: 60
Daily specials
Kids' menu
Vegetarian menu
No alcoholic beverages

No credit cards

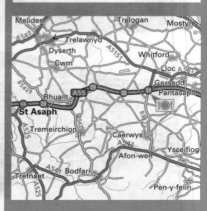

Eatwells Café Restaurant

Thorney Road, Guyhirn, Wisbech PE13 4AD
Tel: 01842 878741

Directions: Travelling east along the A47 between Thorney and Guyhirn, about half a mile before Guyhirn Bridge. Eatwells is next door to Ken Thomas Transport Co.

Eatwells' owner Tracey Wells shows her customers that 'fast food' doesn't all have to taste the same! All Tracey's food is cooked to order and, although she asks for your patience, particularly during busy periods, service is nevertheless prompt and friendly.

A popular item is the 'select-your-own breakfast' with a selection of delicious local sausages at 75p, mushrooms at 55p, or fill your plate with various different vegetables and eggs. Daily specials include stuffed chicken breast, served with potatoes, peas and carrots at £5.25 or vegetarian bean burger with fries and salad at £4.25. Eatwells is handy for road users travelling to the east coast. Sundays roasts at £5.25 are fantastic value. Tracey also offers a takeaway service.

Tracey has put a lot of thought into the refurbishment and layout of the café, which includes a quiet area with comfortable leather chairs, newspapers and a TV.

OPENING TIMES
Mon-Fri:	08.00 - 17.00
Sat:	08.00 - 16.00
Sun;	
Public holidays:	08.00 - 18.00

FACILITIES
Disabled facilities
Newspapers
Parking: cars/trucks: plenty
Caravans/coaches welcome

FOOD AND DRINK
Seating: 42
Outdoor eating area
Daily specials
Kids' menu
Vegetarian menu
Alcoholic beverages

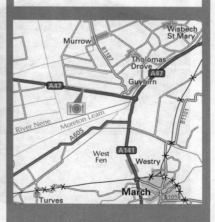

Farm Café and Bar

Washway Road, Fleet Hargate, Holbeach PE12 8LT

Tel: 01406 423652

Directions: On the A17 from King's Lynn and close to town of Holbeach. On north side of road in Fleet Hargate and well signposted. Excellent parking.

Along this stretch of the A17 is a selection of roadside cafés and truckstops. The Farm Café cannot be missed with its bright hoardings, windows with red and yellow striped awnings and hanging flower baskets along the front wall. A long, low building, it houses a large cafeteria, a shop selling toys, collectables, food and drinks, and a stall selling farm-fresh fruit, veg, and plants. There is also a bar, open till 22.30.

The café's low ceiling and stone walls, with pictures and draped red curtains, create an intimate atmosphere. The servery counter has a great selection of menus and fast foods on offer – breakfast menus always being in demand, from the Big Farm bap with two eggs, two sausages and egg at £2.75 to burgers; gammon; pizzas and plaice at varying prices but all good value.

Entertainments include TV and fruit machines.

OPENING TIMES

Mon-Fri:	06.00 - 21.00
Sat:	06.00 - 20.00
Sun:	06.00 - 21.00
Xmas &	
Boxing day:	07.00 - 15.00

FACILITIES

Disabled facilities
Newspapers
Parking: cars: 50; trucks: 50
Caravans/coaches welcome

FOOD AND DRINK

Seating: 200
Daily specials
Kids' menu
Vegetarian menu
Alcoholic beverages

No credit cards

The Fox Inn

Great North Road, Colsterworth, Nr Grantham NG33 5NL
Tel: 01572 767697

Directions: On the A1, approximately 10 miles southbound from Grantham. There is a large sign by the side of the road saying 'The Fox Inn'. From Stamford northbound, there is a cut-through on the A1 to access the Fox Inn.

The Fox Inn, run by Chris Dyson, stands in two acres of landscaped gardens overlooking the Rutland countryside. The exterior of this 16th-century free house is being renovated and sympathetically modernised.

The Fox, has two bars, one has an olde worlde charm with marvellous oak beams and old wood flooring, and an extensive selection of real ales and local beers to choose from. The other bar forms part of the popular restaurant, which serves great roasts from a carvery trolley on Sundays, two courses for £6.95 and three courses for £8.95. There is also an extensive selection on a frequently changing daily menu.

Outside there is a beer garden and patio. The inn also has a function room with its own entrance and facilities. A pool table is available for visitors to enjoy.

OPENING TIMES
Mon-Sat;
Public holidays: 12.00 - 23.00
Sun: 12.00 - 16.00

FACILITIES
Disabled facilities
Washroom for drivers
Parking: cars: plenty; trucks: plenty, refrigerated spaces
Security: lighting, 24-hour CCTV, fenced
Caravans/coaches welcome
Garden

ACCOMMODATION
3 Doubles; 2 Singles;
4 Family: ensuite; TV:
£39.95 (p.p)

FOOD AND DRINK
Seating: plenty
Outdoor eating area
Daily specials; Kids' menu
Vegetarian menu
Alcoholic beverages

Frankie's Café

Old A17, 33 Bridge Road, Sutton Bridge, Spalding PE12 9SH

Tel: 01507 588424

Directions: Travel along the A17 from King's Lynn or Holbeach. At Sutton Bridge take the unclassified road (the old A17) into the village. Frankie's Café is about one mile down from the roundabout and opposite a lay-by, on the north side of the road.

It would be easy to mistake this friendly café for a typical white Fen cottage. However, it is a well-known landmark and a well-established café with a great reputation, frequented by locals and travellers alike. Its low ceiling and beamed room, with many pictures on the walls of trucks from around the world, contribute to the very special atmosphere here. Joyce and Alan keep the hot food coming while talking animatedly with their customers.

Enticing smells from the kitchen are supported by the mouth-watering food that emerges. The daily menu includes a selection of local meats with a large portion of local fresh vegetables, tasting delicious. All-day breakfast includes tea at £3.70. Lunch prices are around £4.00 including a roast meal with two vegetables - perhaps lamb and Yorkshire pudding, two vegetables and potatoes. Also, seasonal salads at £3.50, all freshly supplied local vegetables, and homemade pasties, lasagnes and curries.

OPENING TIMES

Mon-Fri:	07.00 - 14.00
Sat:	07.00 - 13.00
Sun;	
Public holidays:	Closed

FACILITIES

Newspapers
Parking: cars: in front of café;
trucks: in lay-by opposite

ACCOMMODATION

4 Doubles: £17.00 (p.p)
inc. breakfast
4 Singles: £20.00 (p.p)
inc. breakfast

FOOD AND DRINK

Seating: 40
Outdoor eating area
Daily specials; Kids' menu
Vegetarian menu
No alcoholic beverages
No credit cards

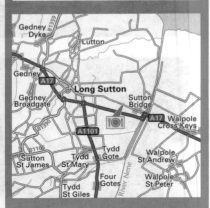

Greedy Pig Café

291 Rockingham Road, Corby NN17 2AE
Tel: 01536 443355

Directions: A6003 Corby to Oakham. At Rockingham roundabout take A6116 (Town Centre).
Over small roundabout and opposite entrance to Jet service station and Aldi store, turn left
through gate in iron fencing into parking area. Greedy Pig signage on road.

This café completely epitomises a traditional English café – always busy, food arrives quickly, without fuss, and is exactly what you would expect.

The café stands in a courtyard surrounded by interesting small shops and is very much a family meeting place, Fridays and Saturdays being particularly busy.

Breakfasts are an important part of the daily menu. Their Pig Feast is the most gi-normous breakfast ever seen, consisting of three times twelve different breakfast items, costing £12.99 and as yet, has never been finished by anyone! Children's breakfasts are £2.95 and veggie breakfasts £4.99.

Owners Matt and Mary also supply takeaway breakfasts, burgers, sausages and chips – you can ring ahead to order and collect.

Bread is supplied daily from a bakery in Corby. My bacon sandwich was absolutely delicious – I commented on the freshness and taste of the bread with its proper crust.

Nearby is Rockingham Castle and Rockingham Motor Speedway.

OPENING TIMES
Tue-Sat:	06.00 - 14.00
Sun-Mon:	07.00 - 14.00
	(van outside)
Public holidays:	Closed

FACILITIES
Disabled facilities
Newspapers
Parking: cars/trucks: plenty
Security: gates locked at night
Caravans welcome
Coaches: no

FOOD AND DRINK
Seating: 32
Outdoor eating area
Daily specials
Kids' menu
No alcoholic beverages

No credit cards

Halfway House

1 Watling Street, Kilsby, Rugby CV23 8YE
Tel: 01788 822888

Directions: The Halfway House is a mile west of Junction 18 of the M1, along the A428. It is on a roundabout at the crossing of the A428 with the A5.

Halfway House is a Victorian public house that now also caters for truckers and other travellers as well as operating as a typical English pub.

Very centrally placed, the Halfway House, run by Mr Singh, is within 30 miles of three major airports, Birmingham, Rugby and Luton. The interior of the building has been modernised in a standard pub style and has the usual public bar with a pool table, fruit machines and TV. The dining room is separate and the pub caters for evening meals. There is a special on the menu everyday, including dishes such as liver and onions with mash and three fresh veg for £5.50. There is also homemade apple pie and custard or chocolate fudge cake for £2.25.

Opposite is a garage with petrol etc. and shops are a five-minute drive away.

OPENING TIMES
Mon-Sun:
Public holidays: 07.00 - 23.00
(food until 21.30)

FACILITIES
Disabled facilities
Newspapers: to read
Cashback
Parking: cars: 20; trucks: 20
Caravans: no
Coaches welcome; Garden

ACCOMMODATION
1 Double; 1 Triple;
1 Quadruple: £17.50 (p.p)
inc. breakfast

FOOD AND DRINK
Seating: 52
Outdoor eating area
Daily specials; Kids' menu
Vegetarian menu
Alcoholic beverages

The Highwayman Café

A64 Malton Road, Stockton on Forest, York YO32 9TL
Tel: 01904 400417

Directions: Off the York ring road. A64 northeast to Scarborough. After Hopgrove roundabout, the Highwayman is easily located on the north side. Brown tourist signs direct visitors in.

With a completed extension and new open-bar food counter, the Highwayman is busier than ever. The staff in this spotlessly clean, pleasantly decorated restaurant are all very friendly and a wooden spoon ordering system speeds delivery during hectic times. On the walls are newspaper cuttings, photographs, local 'wanted' signs of the famous Dick Turpin and his highwaymen, hence the name.

All-day full English breakfast at £4.75 include bread and butter, tea or coffee, a smaller version is £3.95. Homemade specials, one or two each day at £4.50 including tea or coffee, perhaps shepherds pie; roasts; Whitby scampi with chips and salad or gammon and eggs, plus a full range of salads and sandwiches. Large plant pots and hanging flower baskets outside indicate owners Tony and his partner's 'hands-on' role. They are well established here after 14 years.

A pretty walled garden has tables for outside eating – do not be tempted to feed the geese!

OPENING TIMES

Mon-Fri:	07.00 - 16.30
Sat:	07.00 - 15.30
Sun:	08.00 - 15.00

FACILITIES

Washroom for drivers
Newspapers
Parking: cars: plenty;
trucks: in lay-by
Caravans/coaches welcome
Garden
Children's play area

FOOD AND DRINK

Seating: 54
Outdoor eating area
Daily specials
Kids' menu
Vegetarian menu
No alcoholic beverages

No credit cards

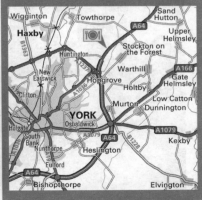

The Hollies

A5 Watling Street, Hatherton, Cannock WS11 1SB
Tel: 01543 503435

Directions: Leave the M6 at Junction 12 and head east along the A5, towards Cannock. The Hollies is a white building on the left, about a mile east of Junction 12.

The café was bought by Mr Halliday in 1961 and is now owned by Mrs M E Halliday. Their daughter now runs it.

Well placed in the centre of England, this is a convenient stopping place for truck drivers who have completed their permitted driving hours for the day.

The café is open all year round and is efficiently run. Staff may prepare themselves for the influx of diners at the usual hours, only to be thwarted if there is a hold-up on the M6, in which case drivers will arrive late, but still want instant service in order to keep within their permitted hours.

The café eating area is completely tiled. There are usually two or three specials on – maybe cottage pie with vegetables and gravy or boeuf bourguignon, costing £3.95. Rhubarb or apple crumble for pudding will set you back 75p.

There's a truck shop upstairs, and accommodation.

OPENING TIMES
Mon–Sun:
Public holidays: 24 hours

FACILITIES
Washroom for drivers (men only)
Newspapers
Parking: cars: 30; trucks: 90, overnight £5.00
Caravans/coaches welcome

ACCOMMODATION
19 Singles: £10.00

FOOD AND DRINK
Seating: 92
Daily specials
Kids' menu
Vegetarian menu
No alcoholic beverages

No credit cards

Jan's Truckstop Café

At Exelby Services, A19 Southbound, Ingleby Arncliffe, Northallerton DL6 3LG
Tel: 07944 444950

Directions: Take the A19 south from Middlesborough. After the A67 turn-off to Yarm, there is a service station, signposted 'Services'. Jan's Café is separate from the filling station and is at the end of the truck park

The restaurant is fresh, clean and light with pine furniture and a long bar with stools along the window side of the café. Proprietor, Janice Atkinson, offers a great selection of freshly made and enticing looking sandwiches, savoury tarts, pies, quiches and salad plates. The café also offers a variety of delicious hot meals including liver and onions; steak and mushroom pie; mince and onion, all priced at £3.90 and including two vegetables, a choice of potatoes and a mug of tea – great value for money.

The restaurant is next to a service station and busy truckstop. Close to the north-eastern seaports, it is a first port of call for many drivers heading south. It's a good stopping place for anyone, not only truck drivers, who wants a break and a quick tasty meal. The staff are friendly and helpful serving the meals, which were arrived promptly from the kitchen.

OPENING TIMES

Mon-Thu:	07.00 - 19.30
Fri:	07.00 - 16.00
Sat-Sun;	
Public holidays:	Closed

FACILITIES

Disabled facilities
Washroom for drivers
Newspapers
Parking: cars: plenty: trucks: plenty in adjacent park, refrigerated spaces
Caravans/coaches welcome

FOOD AND DRINK

Seating: 40
Outdoor eating area
Daily specials
Kids' menu
Vegetarian menu
No alcoholic beverages

No credit cards

Jayne's Place

Bawtry Road, Blyth, Nr Retford S81 8HJ
Tel: 01909 591776

Directions: At A1(M) Junction 34, take A614 to Bawtry. Half a mile up hill on left is Jayne's Place. It is set back from the road with parking in front and behind. It is well signposted some way before the entrance, as the road is a fast one and the café is on top of the hill. Take care if you cross the road.

Established in the 1920s, the interior of this small roadside café is like a Swiss chalet. You immediately feel welcomed due to the atmosphere created by Darren and his friendly staff, the décor of pine-slatted walls, and the use of a soft red colour throughout. In the summer, extra tables are placed outside for customers to eat and enjoy the sunshine and the view.

Jayne's Place may be smaller than other many other cafés but it is always busy with new arrivals throughout its 12-hour opening period. Breakfasts are served all day as well as other traditional English foods. The menu is supplemented with homemade pies, pastries, and puddings, which are very popular.

Although the A614 is a reasonably quiet road, care is needed when leaving the café as it is on a fast stretch of road with a hidden dip.

OPENING TIMES
Mon-Thu:	06.30 - 18.00
Fri:	06.30 - 12.30
Sat-Sun:	06.30 - 12.00
Public holidays:	Closed

FACILITIES
Disabled facilities
Newspapers
Parking: cars/trucks: plenty
Caravans/coaches welcome

FOOD AND DRINK
Seating: 30
Daily specials
No alcoholic beverages

No credit cards

Ashby Road East, Shepshed LE12 9BS
Tel: 01509 507418

Directions: Exit the M1 at Junction 23 and take road to Ashby, A512. The truckstop is the first turning on the right. It is well signposted from the road. Drive round the fenced area to reach the restaurant.

This popular restaurant has a reputation for interesting good food, friendly ambience and pleasant staff. It is pleasant and clean, with fixed tables and chairs and wall-mounted TV. Full breakfasts cost £3.70 (excluding tea or coffee) with all the usual ingredients and are extremely good value for money. You can get burgers or soup or daily specials like chicken Marengo or meat loaf and sauce with peas, cauliflower, rice or potatoes for £4.35 or mixed grills. Fish dishes may be plaice either grilled or deep-fried, or trout with almonds. Pudding such as Bakewell tart or plum crumble are £1.45.

An open cooler stocks cold drinks, chocolate bars and cakes to purchase.

A fully licensed bar also has a pool table and a dartboard. Owner Mr Malek also uses this room for private functions as it has a formal eating area with tables and red velvet banquette seating.

OPENING TIMES
Mon-Fri:	06.00 - 21.00
Sat:	06.00 - 11.00
Sun;	
Public holidays:	Closed

FACILITIES
Washroom for drivers
Newspapers
Parking: cars/trucks: plenty
Security: overnight
Caravans/coaches welcome

FOOD AND DRINK
Seating: 60
Daily specials
Vegetarian menu
Alcoholic beverages
(midday/evenings)

Junction 29 Truckstop M1

Hardwick View Road, Holmwood Ind. Est., Holmwood, Chesterfield S42 5SA
Tel: 01246 856536   Fax 01246 855591

Directions: Leave the M1 at Junction 29 and follow the A6175 to Clay Cross.
Follow the black truck signs to Holmwood Industrial Estate and follow the road
until the big '29' is seen.

Junction 29 Truckstop is about five miles from Chesterfield. Originally the site of a large truck company, it became a truckstop about fifteen years ago so there's plenty of parking available.

A friendly fun team of staff greet you in this well-run stopping venue, owned by Mrs Samantha Plumtree.

The restaurant has a no-smoking area and caters for most culinary tastes. The special meals of the day might be lemon pepper chicken fillet with stir fry vegetables and egg fried rice £5.50 with a choice of desserts including gateaux for £1.45 or peach or coconut crumble served with custard, cream or ice cream for £1.45.

There is a fully licensed bar upstairs plus a large screen TV and live entertainment. Also on site is a fully equipped truckers shop, which can undertake C.B repairs. Diesel is sold 24 hours 7 days a week.

Nearby are the 'Pit Trails' walks.

OPENING TIMES

Mon-Fri: 24 hours
              (06.00 Mon - 12.00 Sat)
Sun;
Public holidays: Closed

FACILITIES

Disabled facilities (some)
Washroom for drivers
Newspapers
Cash machine
Parking: cars: 40; trucks: 130,
overnight £9.50 inc. £2.50 meal
voucher
Security: lighting, patrolled,
CCTV, fenced
Caravans/coaches welcome

FOOD AND DRINK

Seating: 80
Daily specials
Kids' menu
Vegetarian menu
Alcoholic beverages
Credit cards: in shop only

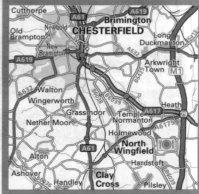

Junction 38 Tebay Truckstop

Junction 38, M6, Old Tebay, Penrith CA10 3SS
Tel: 01539 624505

Directions: Leave M6 at Junction 38, south of Penrith. First left at roundabout, well signposted.

This is an extremely pleasant restaurant with excellent facilities catering for truckers and other road users visiting this beautiful Cumbrian county.

The restaurant occupies a light, spacious glassed area, rather like a conservatory. It is clean and practical with fixed tables and chairs. Breakfasts are always available and the carvery is busy serving fresh hot food from 11.30 to 22.00 hours: a 3-course meal of soup, main course and a sweet costs £7.50, or a two-course meal is just £6.50, or they will cook special meals to order. The food looks wholesome and is certainly good value for money. There is a separate counter for fast food and basic takeaway foods, cakes, sandwiches, drinks etc.

On the walls at the back of the restaurant are wonderful large prints depicting ancient travel methods – packhorses, the fast horse-and-coach service and early Victorian train journeys.

OPENING TIMES
Tue-Sun: 24 hours

FACILITIES
Disabled facilities
Washroom for drivers
Newspapers
Parking: cars/trucks: plenty
Caravans/coaches welcome

FOOD AND DRINK
Seating: 100
Daily specials
Kids' menu
Vegetarian menu
Alcoholic beverages
(Mon-Fri: 18:00–23:00)

Kate's Cabin

Great North Road, A1 Northbound, Chesterton, Peterborough PE7 3UJ
Tel: 01733 235587

Directions: Travelling northbound on the A1(M), between Junction 17 and the A605 Alwalton exit there is a BP service station. Go into the BP service station and Kate's Cabin is next to the station forecourt.

Kate's Cabin is recognisable by the big 'KC' on the façade of this one-storey building. It is very much a 'trunk road' stop with all the facilities one would expect including plenty of truck parking.

Owner Mohammed's menu is pretty much in line with traditional café fare but is well presented and reasonably priced. Full all-day breakfasts are £3.90 – 'bigger' and 'light' versions also available. Daily specials might include sausage, liver and bacon casserole with mash and vegetables for £4.20. Other dishes include ham and egg salads and omelettes and cups of tea for 55p.

In the public bar off the main reception area, is an old pianola for anyone to play – a relaxation from long hours at the wheel. There is also a dartboard.

On the wall is an old road sign showing that Katie's Cabin is 80 miles from London and 147 miles to Scotch Corner.

OPENING TIMES
Mon-Fri: 07.00 - 21.00
Sat: 07.30 - 13.00
Sun; Public holidays: Closed

FACILITIES
Washroom for drivers
Newspapers
Parking: cars: yes; trucks: overnight £5.00 inc. £1.50 food voucher
Caravans/coaches welcome

FOOD AND DRINK
Seating: 66
Daily specials
Kids' menu
Vegetarian menu
Alcoholic beverages
(weekdays 17.00–22.00)

No credit cards

Katie's Kitchen

A1 Southbound, Spital Road, Blyth S81 8EL
Tel: 01909 591102

Directions: Travelling southbound on A1(M), it is after Junction 34 to Blyth. Katie's Kitchen is located opposite the A634 to Maltby.

The interior is prettily furnished with green and white gingham curtains, which gives the café a wonderfully fresh feel. The new owner, Shirley, who took over in spring 2005, is planning many changes once she feels more at home, but one of her first projects is to put up some new exterior signs so that Katie's Kitchen is more visible from the road.

The menu offers wide variety of foods, some making a welcome change from the usual café fare. The salad bar includes salads with crab and prawn, and fresh homemade soup is produced every day. And for afterwards, there is a wonderful jelly bean machine.

Truckers can park up overnight in their parking spaces. However, they don't have any special security arrangements as yet.

Since their first early days the team have settled in well and the car park is comfortably filling up with A1 travellers.

OPENING TIMES
Mon-Sun: 06.45 - 19.00

FACILITIES
Disabled facilities
Newspapers
Parking: cars: plenty; trucks: plenty, refrigerated spaces
Caravans/coaches welcome
Garden
Children's play area

FOOD AND DRINK
Seating: 60
Outdoor eating area
Daily specials
Kids' menu
Vegetarian menu
Alcoholic beverages

The Kitchen

A15 Sleaford Road, Nocton Heath, Lincoln LN4 2AN

Tel: 01522 811299 www.thekitchenatnoctoneath.co.uk

Directions: On A15 halfway between Lincoln and Sleaford, close to B1202 crossroads. Well posted and in clear area.

In an interview by BBC Radio 4, The Kitchen was given the accolade of being 'probably the best truckstop in Lincolnshire'. Previously known as Nocton Heath, The Kitchen was renamed by owners David and Hazel Mather who decided to totally refurbish it, including a modern stylish and larger restaurant – good news to those who have been unable to find a seat here.

David's carvery is a delight to view with fresh daily cooked whole joints of roast meats; our inspector tasted the best roast beef sandwich she had had in a very long time! However, the real speciality is rump steaks - up to 32oz (907g) – a challenge to even the heartiest of eaters! David sources their beef and produce locally, a policy that is reflected in the high quality and variety of food served here. Local ice cream and ales are also on offer.

OPENING TIMES
Mon-Fri: 06.00 - 22.00
Sat: 06.00 - 22.30
Sun;
Public holidays: 09.00 - 17.00

FACILITIES
Disabled facilities
Washroom for drivers
Newspapers
Cash machine
Parking: cars: trucks: plenty, refrigerated spaces (off at 22.00)
Caravans/coaches welcome
Garden
Children's play area

FOOD AND DRINK
Seating: 90
Outdoor eating area
Daily specials; Kids' menu
Vegetarian menu
Alcoholic beverages
(plus local ales)

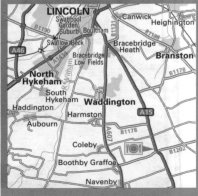

Langrick Station

Main Street, Langrick, Boston PE22 7AH

Tel: 01205 280023

Directions: From Boston on A52/A1121 at Hubbards Bridge Railway Crossing. Take B1192 Langrick. At traffic lights, take right over Iron Bridge. Café is set back a few hundred yards on right, after pub.

Langrick Station re-opened in June 2004. Manageress, Mrs Finney, has worked there for over 10 years and she has plenty of amusing tales to tell. The kitchens have recently been revamped and other work is ongoing.

Standing on the banks of the River Witham, Langrick Station has use of a floating pontoon allowing boats to tie up in the summer months and cross the road to enjoy, amongst other things, one of the house specialities – home-baked sweet pies. Mrs Finney also prepares takeaway food on request – there are plenty of other good homemade dishes to select from.

The walls of the café are festooned with prints of old tractors, motorbikes and trains and there's a plaque commemorating the café's earlier life as a freight and passenger depot, ending in 1967.

The café is on the National Cycle Route, and is a favourite with the veteran motorbike squad.

OPENING TIMES

Mon-Sun: 06.00 - 18.00
Sat-Sun;
Public holidays: Closed

FACILITIES

Newspapers
Parking: cars: plenty; trucks: plenty, refrigerated spaces
Caravans/coaches welcome
Garden

FOOD AND DRINK

Seating: 48
Outdoor eating area
Daily specials
Kids' menu
Vegetarian menu

No credit cards

The Lazy Kettle

A5, Gledrid Roundabout, Weston Rhyn, Oswestry SY11 3EN
Tel: 01691 770066

Directions: A5 between Chirk and Oswestry. The Lazy Kettle is off the big roundabout and at rear of a Total service station.

The Lazy Kettle, owned by James Pidstock Ltd, is a purpose-built café and a good stopping place, Popular with weekend walkers, and cyclists, and appreciated also by truckers travelling between Liverpool to Bristol, the café offers a fast food service. The popular English all-day breakfasts costs £3.90, and a vegetarian version £3.50. The café has an extensive burger menu and a daily specials board offering homemade dishes. I saw a most delicious looking freshly cooked joint of roast beef with Yorkshire pudding, which, along with beef curry with rice, or mince and onions, costs a very reasonable £5.00, including potatoes and vegetables. For fish lovers, a large portion of fish and chips and peas is £5.00.

The café has a TV, also fruit machines. Although the notice at the entrance states there is a licensed bar – there isn't one!

OPENING TIMES

Mon-Fri:	06.00 - 22.00
Sat:	06.00 - 15.00
Sun:	07.00 - 14.00
Public holidays:	Closed

FACILITIES

Disabled facilities
Washroom for drivers
Newspapers; at garage
Parking: cars/trucks: plenty
Caravans/coaches welcome

FOOD AND DRINK

Seating: 50
Outdoor eating area
Daily specials
Kids' menu
Vegetarian menu
No alcoholic beverages

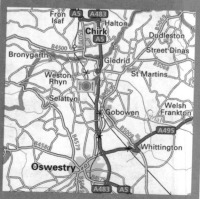

The Lazy Trout Café

A49, Little Stretton, Church Stretton SY6 6RG
Tel: 01694 781282

Directions: A49 south of Shrewsbury, after Church Stretton and before the Craven Arms, set back on right-hand side of road – well signposted, with adjacent car and truck park.

In one of the prettiest locations in Shropshire, by a stream, you will find the charming Lazy Trout Café, with a peaceful and pretty garden. The café was named by two drivers who, after an evening stroll and trying unsuccessfully to entice a large fish from under a bridge, gave up and called it a lazy trout – and the name was taken up by the then café owner.

Mick and Jeanne Farmer have owned the café for the last eighteen years. They offer good home cooking at very reasonable prices. There are regulars that come every day for their lunch, and Jeanne does not start preparing their vegetables until they arrive so that nothing is spoilt. Fish is on the menu but never trout, only cod! The café holds a restaurant licence.

Inside is a model of the café, now a collector's item, made by Corgi Toys.

OPENING TIMES

Mon-Fri:	07.00 - 15.00
Sat:	08.00 - 12.00
Sun;	
Public holidays:	Closed

FACILITIES

Disabled facilities
Washroom for drivers
Newspapers
Parking: cars/trucks: plenty
Caravans/coaches welcome
Garden
Children's play area

FOOD AND DRINK

Seating: 50
Outdoor eating area
Daily specials
Kids' menu
Vegetarian menu
Alcoholic beverages

No credit cards

Leeming Café

Great North Road, Leeming Bar, Bedale DL8 1DT
Tel: 01677 422122

Directions: Located just off the A1 at the Bedale/Northallerton A684 junction –
10 miles south from Scotch corner and one mile from Bedale town centre.
Follow signs for service area.

Close to the dales and moors, the café is a stopping place with a large car park, the site including a restaurant, a café, a collectables shop, and a local-food shop.

The café run by Suzanne Bailes, is modern, light and airy, the walls having murals depicting local attractions and lifelike people in different stances, skilfully painted by artist Lynn Ward.

Food is served from a counter offering a variety of hot and cold meals, as well as takeaway and fast service for those in a rush. The 'Famous 5' breakfast (five cooked items), costs £3.70 and specials include local sausages and a selection of hot savouries; pies and jacket potatoes. Cottage pie and chicken curry are between £6.50 – £7.50. Pot of tea, £1.79.

The more formal Market Square restaurant is popular for its home-cooked food, and is often fully booked on Sundays.

The adjacent Lodge offers accommodation and conference facilities.

OPENING TIMES
Mon-Sun;
Public holidays: 07.00 - 22.00

FACILITIES
Disabled facilities
Washroom for drivers
Newspapers; Cash machine
Parking: cars: plenty;
trucks: plenty
Caravans/coaches welcome
Garden
Children's play area

ACCOMMODATION
In adjacent Lodge

FOOD AND DRINK
Seating: 130
Outdoor eating area
Daily specials
Kids' menu
Vegetarian menu
Alcoholic beverages

Let's Eat Café

On A49 Tarporley Road, Lower Whitley WA4 4EZ
Tel: 01928 717332

Directions: M56 Chester to Manchester. Leave at Junction 10 and take A49 southbound. Café, with bright red signage, is on your left before A533.

A red theme is used throughout the café, making it a cheerful and bright place to stop. The new proprietor, Madeleine Heath, took over in June 2004 and has put her own stamp on the café. Her interior design and menu choices are slightly different from other cafés. An Atkins' diet breakfast at £4.00, full English breakfast at £3.60 and a BIG breakfast at £5.00 are always popular. All her food is prepared on site and she uses as much fresh local produce as possible. Braised steak, or roast pork at £4.50, BLTs at £3.00 with 25p for any extras looked really delicious. Puddings start at £1.50.

I noted a special table with chairs set aside for those clients wearing overalls – which I thought was a very good idea!

There are daily newspapers and a TV for light entertainment.

OPENING TIMES

Mon:	08.00 - 18.00
Tue-Thu:	07.30 - 18.00
Fri:	07.30 - 16.30
Sat:	07.30 - 13.00
Sun;	
Public holidays:	08.30 - 13.00

FACILITIES
Disabled facilities
Washroom for drivers
Newspapers
Parking: cars/trucks: plenty
Caravans/coaches welcome

FOOD AND DRINK
Seating: 100
Daily specials
Kids' menu
Vegetarian menu
No alcoholic beverages

No credit cards

The Limes Café

Old Rufford Road, Bilsthorpe, Newark NG22 8TH
Tel: 01623 411254

Directions: Three miles south of Ollerton on A614 and a mile and a half north of the roundabout with the A617, at the village of Bilsthorpe. The café is painted a lime green.

Originally built as a bungalow in the 1930s, the building is 'arrow' shaped, with the door at its 'point'. It has been a café for at least fifty years and the present proprietor Mark Harrison has run it for the last three.

The café is light and airy with large windows opening onto the Nottinghamshire countryside. In addition to the usual menu, the specials on offer on the day we visited were roast beef, curry (beef) or meat balls for £4.15; steak and kidney pudding; mint lamb pudding; chicken and leek pudding £4.40 and for dessert, treacle sponge or spotted dick £1.85 and apple crumble £1.60, all served with custard, cream or ice cream.

Since Mark took over the business, custom has exceeded all expectations and on a summer weekend, drivers will wait in their cars for a table to become available.

OPENING TIMES

Mon-Fri:	07.00 - 18.00
Sat:	07.00 - 17.00
Sun:	06.30 - 16.00
Public holidays:	10.00 - 16.00

FACILITIES

Parking: cars: 30; trucks: 40, overnight £8.00 inc. evening meal/breakfast/drinks
Caravans/coaches welcome
Garden

FOOD AND DRINK

Seating: 60
Outdoor eating area
Daily specials
Kids' menu
Vegetarian menu
No alcoholic beverages

No credit cards

Little Bistro

A1 Southbound, Bedale DL8 2JJ
Tel: 01845 567990

Directions: On the A1 southbound, about 12 miles from Scotch Corner and before the A61 to Ripon. The Little Bistro is set back in a lay-by and is well signposted from the A1.

Don't be put off by the rough drive and entrance into this café/bistro, it really is a great place. The young staff are very friendly and attentive team, a credit to the proprietor, Ann Richards.

A pleasant entrance opens onto the bistro and an attractive modern lean-to glass conservatory which, with its pine floor and modern pine furniture, is a great addition to the bistro. The two areas are separated by a glass door so that one can be used for private events.

The recently decorated and re-furnished café is spacious with a nice fresh feel. Menus offer roast meals at £5.50; fisherman's pie at £4.50, breakfasts that start £5.20 and a Bistro brunch at £4.90. Light snacks starting at £2.70 include the usual selection of chicken, and beef burgers. Puddings like lemon meringue pie or sponge puddings cost £1.50.

On sale: gifts, including bright red T-shirts.

OPENING TIMES

Mon-Fri:	06.30 - 22.00
Sat:	08.00 - 16.00
Sun:	09.00 - 16.00
Public holidays:	08.00 - 16.00

FACILITIES
Disabled facilities
Washroom for drivers
Newspapers
Parking: cars/trucks: plenty
Caravans: no
Coaches welcome

FOOD AND DRINK
Seating: 60
Daily specials
Kids' menu
Vegetarian menu
No alcoholic beverages

No credit cards

Lodge Farm Café

Washway Road, Fleet, Holbeach PE12 8LT
Tel: 01406 425855

Directions: Situated on the A17 Holbeach to King's Lynn road, in the village of Fleet Hargate. Set back behind lay-by on north side, by turn-off to Holbeach Hurn.

Lodge Farm Café has recently got new owners, a young couple. Their initial aim is to bring the right food at the right price to the table, which they seem to be achieving.

Their long opening hours reflect the Kaymaks' intention to provide a service for their customers and in particular the daily delivery drivers visiting the flower wholesalers in the area. The café is quite small as only the front area is being used at the moment. However this makes it very cosy and provides a pleasant atmosphere in which to enjoy a meal. The foods are basic comfort fast foods.

There is a pool table and licensed bar in adjoining rooms which are due to be refurbished and re-opened in the near future.

OPENING TIMES
Mon-Thu:	07.00 - 21.00
Fri-Sun:	07.00 - 19.00

FACILITIES
Disabled facilities
Newspapers
Parking: cars: 20; trucks: 30, and in adjacent lay-by
Caravans/coaches welcome

FOOD AND DRINK
Seating: 60
Daily specials
Kids' menu
Vegetarian menu
Alcoholic beverages

No credit cards

Lord Stones Café

Lord Stones Country Park, Chop Gate, Stokeley, Middlesbrough TS9 7JH
Tel: 01642 778227   www.lordstones.com

Directions: A172 Middlesbrough to A19 Thirsk. Take road off to Carlton-in-Cleveland. Drive through this attractive village and up a windy road to Chop Gate (approximately two miles). Lord Stones is hidden on the left-hand side. Drive slowly or you'll miss the entrance to it. There is no signage so if you go over the peak and start descending you will have missed the café.

High up at the peak of Chop Gate, and set into the hillside is this very attractive café, worth the drive up this narrow, windy road with amazing views over the North Yorkshire moors.

You can sit and enjoy the open space at tables outside, or inside there's a glowing fire at one end of the café.

Beer from the John Smith brewery is £1.00 a pint, and the drinking water, freshly drawn from the spring in the café, is crystal clear and cold – it's magical. You can fill your own containers for no charge.

Most of the food is sourced locally with fresh vegetables on each plate. Meals include steak pie; sausage and leek pie; roast pork or roast ham served with vegetables at £6.50.

Homemade soup and a roll is £2.50, and there are also homemade scones on offer.

Sandwiches are made to order at £2.00.

OPENING TIMES
Mon-Sun;
Public holidays: 09.00 - 17.00

FACILITIES
Disabled facilities
Newspapers
Parking: cars: 60; trucks: no
Caravans/coaches: no

FOOD AND DRINK
Seating: 50
Outdoor eating area
Daily specials
Kids' menu
Vegetarian menu
Alcoholic beverages

Lorraine's Truckstop

A41 Chester Road, Ternhill, Market Drayton TF9 2JQ
Tel: 01630 638866

Directions: On the A41 from Whitchurch to Junction 3 on M54, about a mile south from the Ternhill roundabout on west side – behind petrol station.

Anyone who has travelled the A41 regularly will have heard of the Halfway House Services café and motel, here since 1932. Recently the café changed hands, but the staff has remained the same so little has changed except the name.

The café is clean and fresh with light cream walls, green and white gingham curtains and green chairs making it a pleasant and light stopping place. Staff are friendly and obviously know their regular customers well. The full all-day breakfasts are £4.95 and the '3-2-1' breakfasts are £2.95 (3 bacon, 2 eggs and 1 toast). Main meals of roasts cost £3.95, and puddings like spotted dick and crumbles are £2.20. The menu also has a great variety of other appetizing dishes. The café has a separate room with a cosy bar operating with full beverage licence: open 11.00–23.00 weekdays.

Accommodation here is basic and clean, in motel style. There's plenty of parking.

OPENING TIMES
Mon-Fri: 06.00 - 23.00
Sat: 07.00 - 16.00
Sun;
Public holidays: 09.00 - 14.00

FACILITIES
Washroom for drivers
Newspapers
Parking: cars/trucks: plenty
Caravans/coaches welcome

ACCOMMODATION
3 Double: £15.00 (p.p)
3 Twin rooms: £15.00 (p.p)
2 Single rooms: £15.00 (p.p)

FOOD AND DRINK
Seating: 54
Daily specials
Kids' menu
Vegetarian menu
Alcoholic beverages

Lynn's Raven Café

A41/A49 Junction, Prees Heath, Whitchurch SY13 3JT

Tel: 01948 665691

Directions: South of Whitchurch at junction of A49 and A41, the café is behind the lay-by.

Lynn's Raven has a reputation of serving the best all-day breakfast in Shropshire! This café serves good food from a varied and imaginative menu, at great value. Everyone is given a warm welcome including bikers, and lorry drivers who take priority as they have their schedules to keep

There is a variety of breakfasts on offer, from the famed all-day breakfast at £4.20 to 'Gut Buster' at £5.60: 3 sausages, 2 eggs, fried bread, 2 bacon, mushrooms, bubble and squeak, beans, tomatoes, hash browns, bread & butter, tea or coffee! There's also a vegetarian version at £5.20.

Roast dinners are served all day, all food freshly cooked to order on the premises using fresh produce. People come for miles for the renowned steak pie.

All desserts are homemade and include spotted dick and sponges served with fresh cream or ice cream for £1.80.

There's also a pool table and TV.

OPENING TIMES

Mon:	07.00 - 20.00
Tue-Thu:	06.00 - 20.00
Fri:	06.00 - 19.00
	(22.00 in summer)
Sat-Sun;	
Public holidays:	07.00 - 15.00
Xmas Day, Boxing Day	
& New Year's Day:	Closed

FACILITIES

Washroom for drivers
Newspapers; Cash machine in adjacent garage
Parking: cars: plenty; trucks: plenty, overnight £6.00 inc.
shower;Security: lighting
Caravans/coaches welcome
Garden; Children's play area

FOOD AND DRINK

Seating: 100
Outdoor eating area
Daily specials; Kids' menu
Vegetarian menu
No alcoholic beverages
No credit cards

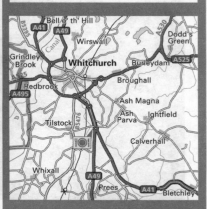

Mainsgill Farmshop and Tea Room

East Layton, Richmond DL11 7PN
Tel: 01325 718 860

Directions: From Scotch Corner on the A1, take the A66 going north. Mainsgill Farm is opposite the junction for East Layton. Set well back from the A66.

Within a farm building complex with open fields and views in front of the café is the Mainsgill Farmshop and Tea Room. Maria Hewshaw and her husband started up nearly five years ago selling farm fresh produce and have a thriving business. Their own butchers prepare meats, sausages, steak pies and burgers either to enjoy in their pleasant restaurant, or to take away in vacuum packs. Their all-day breakfasts use their own bacon and freshly laid free-range eggs. Plans are afoot to extend the restaurant.

Homemade preserves, jams and chutneys, biscuits and cakes are also for sale. Some visitors leave their order and collect it on their return journey from holiday.

The fields in front of the café surprise you with guinea fowl, llamas, ostriches, Shetland ponies, Jacob sheep and some unusual poultry – it is a great joy to hear the children's excitement at seeing these animals running free.

OPENING TIMES
Mon-Sun:
Public holidays: 09.00 - 17.00

FACILITIES
Disabled facilities
Parking: cars/trucks: plenty
Caravans/coaches welcome
Garden
Children's play area

FOOD AND DRINK
Seating: 32
Outdoor eating area
Daily specials
Kids' menu
Vegetarian menu
No alcoholic beverages

Markham Moor Truckstop

Markham Moor, Retford DN22 0QU
Tel: 01777 838921

Directions: On the A1 on the roundabout at Markham Moor between Newark and Retford. Follow the exit off the roundabout with the 'Lorry Park' sign and the sign to Walesby and Milton. The truckstop is behind a Travel Lodge and Shell petrol station.

A very well-managed roadside stopover run by Mr and Mrs Jubb. The café looks as though it was purpose built and there is a real feeling of efficiency and organisation. The reception area is welcoming and spacious and it is very clean throughout.

The restaurant is counter service only but again, there is plenty of space for tables and lots of natural daylight. The food served is standard but good English fare with healthy portions for the larger appetite. The favourite here is the big English breakfast that includes all the usual ingredients, and a few more specials.

There is a quiet area set aside with comfortable leather chairs and a TV set. For the true trucker enthusiasts, there are models of various miniature trucks for sale. Also for the truckers, there's secure floodlit parking, overnight patrols and parking for refrigerated trucks. This is a very popular venue.

OPENING TIMES
Mon:	06.00 - 22.00
Tue-Fri:	05.30 - 22.00
Sat:	05.30 - 10.00

FACILITIES
Disabled facilities
Washroom for drivers
Newspapers
Cash machine
Parking: cars: plenty; trucks: plenty, refrigerated spaces
Security: floodlight, overnight patrols
Caravans/coaches welcome

FOOD AND DRINK
Seating: 240
Daily specials
Kids' menu
Vegetarian menu
No alcoholic beverages

No credit cards

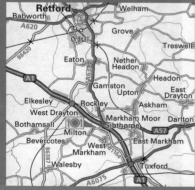

The Meadows Inn

Chequers Road, Cattle Market, West Meadows Industrial Estate, Derby DE21 6EP
Tel: 01652 680966

Directions: From M1, exit Junction 25 and take A52 to Derby. Follow road in until you come to major large roundabout 'Pentagon Island'. Take first left off to industrial area, then first left again. The Meadows is in the Derby cattle market, well signposted on your right-hand side.

This Inn has been here for about 25 years and today is widely used by truck drivers and locals during the week as the public bar is a popular meeting place. At weekends when car boot sales are held in the market, there's a constant flow of customers, wanting either beer or cooked breakfasts!

Managed by Angela Gibb, the Inn serves all-day breakfasts, burgers, sandwiches and basket snacks plus a full menu including haddock, peas, fries and salad at £4.25; steak, kidney and ale pie, or gammon, fries, egg or pineapple in the £4.00 range.

The public bar has a pool table, dartboard and slot machines and there's a larger room used for entertainments, auctions, caged bird shows and others, the versatility of the room ensuring it is well used and appreciated.

A pleasant atmosphere runs throughout the whole establishment and the staff are very welcoming and pleasant.

OPENING TIMES

Mon-Wed: 10.00 - 15.00
16.30 - 12.00 Midnight
Thu: 09.00 - 12.00 Midnight
Fri: 10.00 - 12.00 Midnight
Sat; Sun: Licensing hours only

FACILITIES

Disabled facilities
Washroom for drivers
Parking: cars/trucks: plenty
Caravans/coaches welcome

FOOD AND DRINK

Seating: 100
Daily specials
Kids' menu
Vegetarian menu
Alcoholic beverages

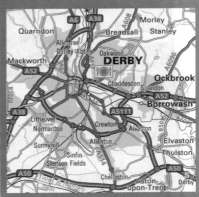

Midway Truckstop

Prees Heath, Whitchurch SY13 3JT
Tel: 01948 663160

Directions: South of Whitchurch on roundabout where A49 to Shrewsbury and A41 to Newport split. Midway Truckstop is just 200 yards along the lay-by, behind car park. Well signposted, it is easy to locate.

The Burkes family has run this café for over 18 years and it is currently in the capable hands of Philip, who opens the café early every morning.

An old-style café, it has managed to retain its charm. It even has old wooden school chairs and table desks. A tiny room off the main café is a quiet relaxation space with comfortable chairs, TV and paperbacks. Fruit machines are the other end of the café!

On the menu (you'll find a truckstop newsletter included) are standard café dishes as well as 'A Healthy Option' breakfast at £4.00, plus 'Extra caviar with toast' £1.90, special cottage pie and salads, in fact a range of less usual home-cooked meals.

A small enclosed flower garden at the side of the café has tables for outside eating.

When the annual 'Bikers Bash' is held, the Midway stays open till the last one leaves!

OPENING TIMES
Mon-Fri: 05.45 - 20.00
Sat: 05.45 - 18.00
Sun;
Public holidays: 07.00 - 15.00

FACILITIES
Washroom for drivers
Newspapers
Parking: cars/trucks: plenty
Caravans/coaches welcome
Garden

FOOD AND DRINK
Seating: 56
Daily specials
Kids' menu
Vegetarian menu
No alcoholic beverages

No credit cards

Motorman's Café

Manchester Road, Marsden, Nr Huddersfield HD7 6NJ
Tel: 01484 844428

Directions: A62 from Huddersfield to Oldham – east end of Marsden village, off road on hillside. Parking is in front of café.

Slightly off the beaten track but set in the astounding setting of the Pennines is the Motorman's Café. Few truckers stop here as it is not on a well-travelled truck route. However, plenty of visitors frequent the café and keep it busy.

Jean Hall has been here since 1978 and has made the café a popular stopping place – ideal for a hearty breakfast before tackling the moors. Breakfasts include tea/coffee, bread and butter or toast and cost £3.10–£4.50. The lunch menus have a variety of dishes including salads and omelette from £3.00–£4.50. Puddings like lemon sponge with lemon zest with custard or ice cream at only £1.50 are excellent value. I also saw a delicious looking selection of homemade cakes, biscuits, and buttered teacakes.

Sunday lunch menus at around £6.00 include roasts and salmon dishes, with all the trimmings. It is obvious why this venue is so popular.

OPENING TIMES

Mon-Fri: 07.30 - 14.00
Sun: 09.00 - 17.00
Sat;
Public holidays: 07.00 - 18.00

FACILITIES

Newspapers
Parking: cars/trucks: plenty
Caravans: no
Coaches: advance notice required

FOOD AND DRINK

Seating: 36
Daily specials
Kids' menu
Vegetarian menu
No alcoholic beverages

No credit cards

Necton Diner

A47 Norwich Road, Necton, Nr Swaffham PE37 8DQ

Tel: 01760 724180

Directions: On the A47 between Swaffham and Dereham. Necton village is about a mile east from the end of the dual carriageway out of Swaffham. Next to T S Commercials (old filling station).

Necton Diner, run by Linda and Jay, could be mistaken for a cowboy frontier café from the outside, and inside, the bright colours – walls are yellow – in the large eating and entertainment area continue that theme. Owners and staff wear black and white chequered outfits, adding to the colourful atmosphere.

This is a good stopping place, easy to access with lots of parking space. Big all-day breakfasts cost £4.50 and includes free refills of tea and coffee; other choices on the menu include sausages and mash; shepherds pie; baked potatoes with various fillings, as well as a selection of English puddings: treacle tart, bread and butter pudding with custard or ice cream, to name just a few, all reasonably priced at £2.10. The sizes of the portions are extremely generous.

The drinks fridge holds a good supply of cold drinks – cans of Red Bull, lagers, beers and alcoholic mixes.

OPENING TIMES

Mon-Fri:	07.30 - 21.00
Sat-Sun:	08.00 - 14.00
Public holidays:	08.00 - 16.00

FACILITIES

Washroom for drivers
Parking: cars: plenty; trucks: plenty, overnight £10.00 includes food voucher for £5.25
Caravans/coaches welcome

FOOD AND DRINK

Seating: 100
Daily specials
Alcoholic beverages

No credit cards

155

Norfolk Dumpling

Livestock Market, Hall Road, Norwich NR4 6DW
Tel: 01603 451392

Directions: Enter Norwich and get onto the City's ring road. Follow the clear signs for 'Livestock Market' and 'Holiday Inn' on Hall Road.

The café, in the once-busy livestock market, is still a popular meeting place. Car boot sales and the fortnightly livestock auctions bring in the customers for the café's basic fast food – burgers, buns and chips all day. Breakfasts are the most popular but other specials include half roast chickens with all the trimmings at £3.25 and there's a selection of savoury pies and sausages.

Mr Wells' café also has a large function room with a raised stage and dance floor for live entertainment like jazz or country music nights, or for private meetings. It has a fully licensed bar.

The 'drivers' bar is behind the function room – truckers use this nightly after eating in the café. They have a pool table and a bar, open daily from 12.00 noon to 23.00 hours, excluding Sundays when it closes after lunch. Plenty of parking in the Cattle Market.

OPENING TIMES

Mon-Fri:	07.00 - 15.00
Sun:	07.00 - 13.00
Sat;	
Public holidays:	Closed

FACILITIES
Washroom for drivers
Parking: cars/trucks: plenty
Caravans/coaches welcome

FOOD AND DRINK
Seating: 100
Daily specials
Alcoholic beverages

No credit cards

NT Truckstop

A5 Watling Street, Clifton-upon-Dunsmore, Rugby CV23 0AE
Tel: 01788 535115   Fax: 01788 561284

Directions: Leave the M1 at Junction 18. Follow A5 through a series of roundabouts for about three miles. The truckstop is on the right-hand (eastern) side of the road after a long straight section.

The Rugby Truckstop is a large, purpose-built chalet-style building with a large dining area and a restroom with television and easy chairs. At the rear is a function room with a fully equipped bar (drivers will not be served alcohol unless they have an overnight ticket for their trucks).

Linda Jones' café offers a range of daily specials, all priced at £4.99. Dishes include beef and mushroom stew, chilli con carne, and steak and kidney pie. They also do a mixed grill for £5.25 and steak for £6.25. A wide range of deserts includes apple pie and rhubarb crumble at £1.35. For the thirsty traveller there is a bottomless cup of tea for 99p. All good value and well presented. Parking on site is secure, and also on site is an unmanned, fully automated filling station that accepts cards for Key Fuels, Diesel Direct, Croft Fuels and Petrol Plus.

OPENING TIMES

Mon-Fri:	24 hours
Sat:	05.00 - 14.00
Sun:	16.00 onwards
Public holidays:	Closed

FACILITIES

Disabled facilities
Washroom for drivers
Newspapers; Cash machine
Parking: cars: 50; trucks: 260, refrigerated spaces, overnight £10.00/£13.00 inc. meal voucher
Security: lighting, patrolled, CCTV, fenced
Caravans: no
Coaches welcome

FOOD AND DRINK

Seating: 100
Daily specials
Vegetarian menu
Alcoholic beverages

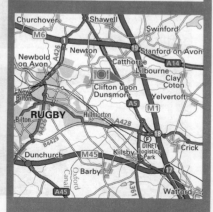

NT Truckstop

Hilton Ind. Est., Cannock Road, Featherstone, Wolverhampton WV10 7HP
Tel: 01902 307535

Directions: Exit at Junction 1 of the M54. Head south and take the left at the roundabout. Alternatively, follow the blue truck signs on the M54.

The NT Wolverhampton Truckstop is one of five previously run by a company called Night Owl, and offering similar facilities at all five locations. The building at Wolverhampton was built in the 1980s – a single-storey building with all the facilities a trucker would require, but with accommodation to be added. This didn't happen.

The facilities offered are electronic security, vehicle recognition cameras, CCTV and electric fencing. There is a fully automated filling station accepting cards from various suppliers – Keyfuels, Petrol Plus etc. In addition there are full shower facilities, a shop, cash machine, bar and television lounge.

All meals, for example lasagne and chicken pie, are under £5.00 except the rump steak, which is £6.00. They all come with chips, mash or jacket potatoes and vegetables. A bottomless cup of tea is 95p.

OPENING TIMES

Mon-Fri:	05.00 - 23.00
Sat:	05.00 - 15.00
Sun:	15.00 - 23.00
Public holidays:	05.00 - 15.00

FACILITIES

Disabled facilities
Washroom for drivers
Newspapers; Cash machine
Parking: cars: 50; trucks: 190, refrigerated spaces
Security: lighting, patrolled, CCTV, fenced.
Caravans: no. Motor homes only. Coaches welcome.
Shop: open: Sun 07.00–Sat: 1600
Garden

FOOD AND DRINK

Seating: 65.
Daily specials
Kids' menu
Vegetarian menu
Alcoholic beverages

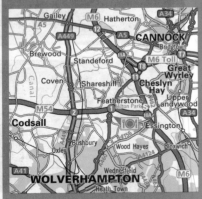

The Oakmere Chef

A556 Chester Road, Oakmere, Northwich CW8 2HB
Tel: 01606 889072

Directions: A556 Northwich to Chester, near the crossroads with the A49 on the south side is the Oakmere Chef. Set back from the road and well signposted.

Four years ago Mr and Mrs Singleton took over the café (formerly a Little Chef), and put their own stamp on the place, starting with a friendly welcome that creates a pleasant atmosphere.

The light and spacious restaurant is comfortably decorated and has designated smoking and no-smoking areas. There's a children's play area full of toys and books, opening onto the café.

Some items on the menu, will appeal to the health conscious in particular. I noticed an 'Atkins' breakfast at £4.75; light continental breakfast at £2.50; and individual cereal packets at 99p. Main meals might include buffalo with red wine at £7.99 or lamb tagine at £3.99. For vegetarians, the harvest bake and penne pasta also looked appetizing.

Customers for afternoon teas can enjoy muffins, pastries, cakes and pancakes, each served with a pot of tea, at £1.75.

The outside area and garden space are well kept and attractive.

OPENING TIMES
Mon-Sun:
Public holidays: 08.00 - 20.00

FACILITIES
Disabled facilities
Newspapers
Parking: cars/trucks: plenty
Caravans/coaches welcome
Garden
Children's play area

FOOD AND DRINK
Seating: 120
Outdoor eating area
Daily specials
Kids' menu
Vegetarian menu
No alcoholic beverages

Peranakan Café and Restaurant

A605 next to Q8 Service Station, Warmington, Oundle PE8 6TZ
Tel: 01832 226497

Directions: Take the A605 travelling between Peterborough and Oundle. Peranakan is on the Warmington roundabout, set back from the road, alongside the Q8 service station.

Set in Northamptonshire countryside, Peranakan is an innovative style of café and restaurant that opened in February 2005. Proprietor June offers a café menu from 07.30 until 17.00 hours every day. This menu includes traditional English fare and homemade cakes plus a range of ciabattas, baguettes and tortilla wraps for those wanting something a little bit different.

However, in the evening Peranakan becomes an oriental restaurant offering delicious Malaysian and Chinese foods from an interesting and varied menu. There are plenty of the favourites as well as a wonderful selection of soups and Peranakan specials, all reasonably priced between between £4.25–£4.75 an item. If you do not have the time to enjoy the atmosphere of this thriving restaurant, then a takeaway service is available. Outside, there are tables and chairs on a grassy bank and a green space where children can run safely.

OPENING TIMES
Mon-Fri: 07.30 - 17.00
Sat-Sun:
Public holidays: 09.30 - 13.00
Chinese Restaurant: 18.00–21.30

FACILITIES
Disabled facilities
Cash machine in filling station
Parking: cars: 25; trucks: in lay-by
Caravans/coaches welcome
Garden

FOOD AND DRINK
Seating: 40
Outdoor eating area
Vegetarian menu
Alcoholic beverages

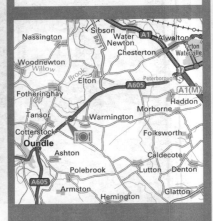

Poplar 2000

Cliffe Lane, Lymm, Nr Warrington WA13 0SP
Tel: 01925 757777   Fax 01925 735190

Directions: M6 Junction 20, close to M56 Junction 9. Follow A50 towards Knutsford. Poplar 2000 is part of Lymm Truckstop. Well signed.

A pleasant break from motorway driving, the whole complex is well maintained by manager Andrew Schmacher. All the facilities are around an unusual courtyard, which includes life-size wood-carved cowboys. For truckers there are full truckstop facilities including a well-stocked convenience store and C. B. shack, a barber's shop and H.G.V diesel. The large café/canteen operates a carvery counter offering a range of breakfasts from £1.30 to toasted egg specials at £4.05. Roast beef and Yorkshire pudding, and other specials, start at £4.95. Homemade pies £2.05 and a range of English hot puddings from £1.25, with pieces of fresh fruit at 45p. There is a designated non-smoking area within the café. TV screens show Sky and local programmes – the special TV room is a quiet room. A pool table is also available. The licensed bar upstairs operates evenings Monday to Friday.

OPENING TIMES
Mon-Sun: 24 hours

FACILITIES
Disabled facilities
Washroom for drivers
Telephone/fax
Newspapers
Cash machine
Parking: cars/trucks: plenty
Caravans/coaches welcome

FOOD AND DRINK
Seating: 250
Daily specials
Vegetarian menu
Alcoholic beverages
(Mon-Fri: 17.30–23.00.
Closed: Sat–Sun)

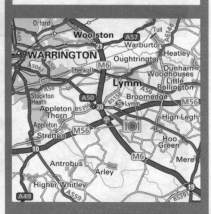

Poplar 2000 Café

Barton Lorry Park, Barton, Richmond DL10 6NA

Tel: 01325 377777

Directions: Leave A1(M) at Junction 56. Follow sign to Barton. Poplar 2000 Café is on right, behind BP petrol station and adjacent to the Truckstop. Well signposted.

The café is built on a hill and easily accessible from the A1. It has been in the capable hands of 'young' Wendy Pattinson for 21 years, so she knows her regular truckers and customers, though everyone gets a warm welcome. This creates a very happy and friendly atmosphere. In the spacious and light restaurant, breakfasts are from £3.49 up to £4.49. Specials on the daily board are liver and bacon; shepherds pie or roast beef at £4.99. Desserts such as jam roll or apple pie are from £1.79. The menu is very varied and changes regularly, and the restaurant also has a licence for alcohol.
A TV room is available for drivers to relax in after a long haul on the roads.
With plenty of parking this café is an ideal spot for coaches and caravans to call at, with good facilities and a large reception area.

OPENING TIMES

Mon-Fri:	06.00 - 22.00
Sat:	07.00 - 15.00
Sun:	08.00 - 16.00
Public holidays:	Closed

FACILITIES

Washroom for drivers
Newspapers
Cash machine in filling station.
Parking: cars: plenty; trucks: adjacent park, refrigerated space
Security: CCTV
Caravans/coaches welcome
Garden

FOOD AND DRINK

Seating: 42
Daily specials
Kids' menu
Vegetarian menu
Alcoholic beverages

No credit cards

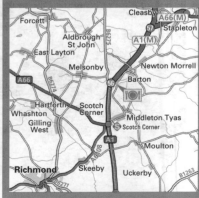

Portly Ford Café

Northampton Road, Welford NN6 6JG
Tel: 01858 575120

Directions: Exit Junction 1 off A14, take A5199 to Husbands Bosworth. 500 yards up on the right. Close to Naseby Battlefield (1645). Five minutes from M6/M1 junction. Do not confuse with the 'Sit-in Café'.

On top of a hill with wonderful open views across the surrounding countryside, the café is inside a bright blue Portakabin. It is in a large truck-parking area, but when the sun shines you can sit at the tables outside and enjoy the amazing scenery.

Cabins are joined together to create a large space and the red and white gingham theme and the red tabards worn by Andrew Miles' staff are colourful and add to the friendly atmosphere. There is a designated non-smoking area.

Daily and evening specials include roast pork and liver and bacon at £4.85 all with fried potato chips, vegetables and gravy, bread and butter, tea or coffee. The daily set meals, similar to those served in the evenings, start at £3.85 to £4.85.

Takeaway burgers and sandwiches are available until 21.45. The café closes at 22.00.

OPENING TIMES
Mon-Thu:	09.00 - 17.00
Fri:	06.00 - 20.00
Public holidays:	Closed

FACILITIES
Newspapers
Parking: cars/trucks: plenty
Caravans/coaches: no

FOOD AND DRINK
Seating: 60
Outdoor eating area
Daily specials
No alcoholic beverages

No credit cards

Quernhow Café

Great North Road, Nr Thirsk YO7 4LG
Tel: 01845 567221

Directions: Northbound from Junction 49(A61) on the A1. Just before the B6267 is the Quernhow Café. It is opposite a BP filling station. There is a signpost for the café 300 yards (274 metres) up the road. Can be difficult to see if lorry park is full.

Close to the Yorkshire Dales Park, the Quernhow Café, has recently been taken over by Malcolm Daniels who has carried out extensive refurbishment and redecoration. The walls are hung with pictures of different types of old transport: trains, motorbikes, buses and cars and there is now a separate no-smoking area.

The menu shows great variety and many of the ingredients are sourced locally. As well as the usual breakfasts, pies and sausages there is a good selection of roasts including duck and pheasant.

The accommodation has also been redecorated and the per-night price includes breakfast and an evening meal – a real bargain.

Also on the property is a static and drive-in caravan park, ideally placed off the A1 northbound for a night stop over.

OPENING TIMES
Mon-Sun: 24 hours

FACILITIES
Disabled facilities
Washroom for drivers
Newspapers
Parking: cars/trucks: plenty
Caravans/coaches welcome
Garden
Children's play area

ACCOMMODATION
7 double rooms: ensuite; TV:
£39.50 per night inc.
evening meal and breakfast

FOOD AND DRINK
Seating: 120
Outdoor eating area
Daily specials
Kids' menu
Vegetarian menu
Alcoholic beverages

The Ranch

The Old Great North Road, Newark NG24 1BY
Tel: 01636 611198

Directions: In the cattle market, close to the centre of Newark town, heading north. Follow the old A1 through town, past the castle, over the river bridge and level crossing. Cattle market is on the right.

The Ranch Café serves the truck park adjacent to the cattle market. It's close to the town centre, so most requirements of the truck drivers can be met within easy walking distance.

The café is quite comfortable and modern, with full shower facilities for the truckers. Owner Richard Cox supplies main meals that include casseroles; chilli; curry; lasagne and meat and potato pie, all priced at £4.10. Desserts, at £1.60 include bread and butter pudding, and crumbles served with ice cream. The town itself has many historic connections, being in Robin Hood country, and on the Old Great North Road. It has a very attractive market place and a splendid church, but the most prominent building is the fine medieval castle ruins, standing on the banks of the River Trent. Newark is also host to a monthly antiques fair with dealers selling extraordinary items from all parts of the world.

OPENING TIMES
Mon-Fri: 06.00 - 22.00
Sat-Sun;
Public holidays: Closed

FACILITIES
Disabled facilities
Washroom for drivers
Parking: cars: 50; trucks: 100, overnight £10.00 inc. £3.00 for meal
Security: lighting, patrolled, CCTV
Caravans/coaches welcome

FOOD AND DRINK
Seating: 39
Daily specials, Kids' menu
Vegetarian menu
No alcoholic beverages

No credit cards

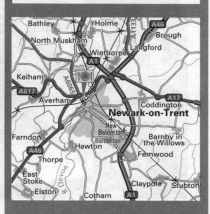

Redbeck Motel

Doncaster Road, Crofton, Wakefield WF4 1RR

Tel: 01924 862730

Directions: On the A638, exit at Junction 38 of A1(M) towards Wakefield. Through Ackworth Moor is the village of Crofton – The Redbeck is situated on the south side, next to a Shell petrol station.

This long-established, family owned 24-hour diner is always busy, with efficient staff under owner Peter Worth providing the ideal quick service required. Good quality food just keeps on coming from the kitchen, and still the restaurant is tidy and the tables clean. The 'Famous Breakfast' is a popular favourite. High chairs are available for children.

The games machines in the main restaurant are used by all age groups. In a separate room there are two pool tables, while the residents' lounge is quieter with comfy chairs and a TV. In front of the motel are tables for eating at, with a fenced play area for children and with patio seating alongside, so you can keep an eye on them.

Al's Café Bar, with cocktail menu, is fresh and inviting. It adjoins the diner and opens Monday to Friday 17.00–23.00, and all day at weekends.

OPENING TIMES
Mon-Sun;
Public holidays: 24 hours

FACILITIES
Disabled facilities
Newspapers; Cash machine
Parking: cars: plenty; trucks: plenty, refrigerated spaces
Security: collect key from 24-hour café
Caravans: no; Coaches welcome
Children's play area

ACCOMMODATION
5 Doubles: ensuite; TV: £34.00 inc. breakfast
11 Singles (basic): £17.00 inc. breakfast

FOOD AND DRINK
Seating: 50
Outdoor eating area
Daily specials; Kids' menu
Vegetarian menu
Alcoholic beverages

Riverside Café

A47/A1, Picnic Area, Wansford, Peterborough PE5 7XF
Tel: 0795 6699928

Directions: Exit the A1 at Junction 17 for the A47 and head for Peterborough. Café is at the first turn right (before the petrol station), opposite Sacrewell Farm.

The Riverside Café is in a picnic area, overlooking the River Nene with its swans and river boats. There is plenty of parking for cars and trucks.

The café is a Portakabin in which you can buy specials, usually cooked towards the evening, that include roasts of gammon, chicken, pork, all served with vegetables and mashed potato, or salad and chips for between £4.50–£5.00. For dessert: bread and butter pudding with custard or fresh cream, and crumbles or homemade pies with custard or cream are £1.50. There are also fresh apples, bananas and oranges.

Jackie, the new owner, has recently made improvements and plans to put tables outside on the grass so customers can eat while enjoying the view. The café has no outside toilet, but 100 yards (91 metres) away there are public toilets. The nearby filling station is open 24/7.

OPENING TIMES
Mon-Fri: 07.00 - 20.00
Sat: 07.00 - 12.00
Sun;
Public holidays: 08.00 - 16.00
                  (summer only)

FACILITIES
Newspapers: read only
Parking: cars: 40; trucks: 20
Caravans/coaches welcome
Garden

FOOD AND DRINK
Seating: 40
Outdoor eating area
Daily specials
Kids' menu
Vegetarian menu
No alcoholic beverages

No credit cards

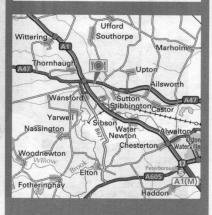

The Roman Café

A52 Bridge End Road, Ropsley, Grantham NG32 3AD

Tel: 01476 576477

Directions: On A52 – 5 miles east of Grantham en route to Sleaford. Set back on south side next to the Power petrol station.

The Roman Café is also known as 'the famous chariot stop' – a perfect stopping place on the way to the east coast. This is very much a family concern, owned by Mrs Ireland and Mrs Simpson, with all members helping at the busy times, and a comfortable friendly atmosphere extending throughout. Inside you'll see some interesting black and white photographs of farming in the late 1800s and some fantastic farming memorabilia. Ingredients for the meals are locally sourced where possible. The café is well known for its delicious homemade scones and sponge cakes, which you can buy to take away. There's also a full menu of breakfast foods and hot and cold lunches – the portions are generous and excellent value for money. A light and airy conservatory provides additional seating. Outside there are tables and a safe, enclosed play area for small children.

OPENING TIMES
Mon-Sun;
Public holidays: 07.30 - 16.30
(15.30 winter)

FACILITIES
Newspapers
Parking: cars: 50; trucks 30, refrigerated spaces
Caravans/coaches welcome
Garden
Children's play area

FOOD AND DRINK
Seating: 65
Outdoor eating area
Daily specials
Kids' menu
Vegetarian menu
No alcoholic beverages

No credit cards

Rose and Crown

6 Main Street, Zouch, Loughborough LE12 5EQ
Tel: 01509 842240

Directions: On A6006 between Loughborough and Kegworth, Junction 24 of M1, in village of Zouch by bridge over River Soar.

Alongside the River Soar, with a jetty and towpath where the long boats and barges tie up, is The Rose and Crown, recently taken over by Jacqueline Ashley, who offers breakfasts and appetising meals throughout the day. Breakfasts, from £3.90, are 'hearty' with lots of optional extras and include tea and toast. Sunday lunches with three vegetable selection, potatoes and Yorkshire puds start at £6.95, as well other home cooked dishes, and a selection of scrumptious desserts. Children have their own menus and free ice cream is offered to those who eat up. Curry night on Mondays is very popular with the locals.

The attractive oak-beamed bar operates a full licence and in winter a cosy fire helps to create a warm and very friendly atmosphere. Quality ales and lagers are available.

Outside there's a fenced safe area and gardens with plenty of table and chairs – popular with families.

OPENING TIMES

Mon-Sat:	09.00 - 21.00
Sun;	
Public holidays:	12.00 - 18.30

FACILITIES

Parking: cars: plenty; trucks: a few
Caravans/coaches welcome
Garden
Children's play area

FOOD AND DRINK

Seating: 72
Outdoor eating area
Daily specials
Kids' menu
Vegetarian menu
Alcoholic beverages

The Salt Box Café

A511/A50 Derby Road, Hatton DE65 5PT

Tel: 01283 813189

Directions: On the junction of the old A50 with the A511.
Four miles north of Burton upon Trent and just north of Tutbury.

The airy feel and large windows of this single-storey, purpose-built café slightly gives it the feel of a seaside café. It seems to be a popular eating place, with truckers, married couples and seniors all choosing from an extensive menu of daily specials like Cajun chicken with rice and chips or roast pork and stuffing, followed by apple and rhubarb crumble, jam roly-poly, or cheesecake.

One couple I talked to told me they had met at the Salt Box after having lost their respective spouses. The couple met at this café and agreed to have a morning cup of tea every day before the man went off to work. Sometimes she'd persuade him to phone work to say he was sick, and they would spend the day together. Eventually they married but they still call in here, as it was their 'trysting' place. The café has plenty of parking, with an overnight charge for truckers.

OPENING TIMES

Mon-Fri:	07.00 - 19.00
Sat:	07.00 - 14.00
Sun;	
Public holidays:	Closed

FACILITIES

Disabled facilities
Washroom for drivers
Newspapers
Parking: cars: 70; trucks: 30, overnight £7.50 inc. £2.50 meal voucher.
Security: CCTV, fenced, lighting inside and out
Caravans/coaches welcome
Garden; Children's play area

FOOD AND DRINK

Seating: 140
Daily specials; Kids' menu
Vegetarian menu
Alcoholic beverages

Sand Martin Café

Main Road, Hagworthingham PE23 4LE
Tel: 01507 588424

Directions: Through the pretty village of Hagworthingham in Lincolnshire. Situated on the A158 road between Skegness and Horncastle. Next to closed petrol station.

Open every day of the year except between 20th December and 14th February, the Sand Martin Café, owned by Rachel Mawson, is spotlessly clean and well organised, with modern stylish furniture that works well. The walls are hung with regularly changed artwork from local painters and photographers and which are for sale. Accommodation is also available.

Comments overheard in the restaurant reveal that some customers travel a long way to the Sandmartin in order to sample Rachel's delicious food. Specials of the day might include salmon fillet in a dill and lemon sauce at £6.50, and there's a wide selection of two-course meals from £6.00 to chose from. Bramhill Pottery is about five minutes from the restaurant and is well signposted from the road. Nearby, Horncastle is an attractive market town with plenty of art and antique shops to visit.

OPENING TIMES
Mon-Sun;
Public holidays: 08.00 - 18.00

FACILITIES
Disabled facilities
Parking: cars/trucks: plenty
Caravans/coaches welcome

ACCOMMODATION
1 Double: ensuite: £40
1 Family: ensuite: £40

FOOD AND DRINK
Seating: 60
Daily specials
Kids' menu
Vegetarian menu
Alcoholic beverages

No credit cards

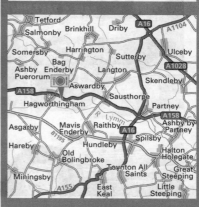

Scoff a Lott Café

186 Hessle Road, Hull HU3 3AD
Tel: 01482 323289

Directions: M62 eastwards becomes A63. Follow along to first roundabout – follow sign to Infirmary. Scoff a Lott Café is opposite the Total service station.

The Scoff-a-Lott Café is on Hessle Road within a row of shops. You can park on the road opposite.

Small, but well known around Hull, it is very much how one imagines an English café: basic, good wholesome food served with enthusiasm. The café serves truckers coming in from Holland on the ferry, and motorcyclists arriving from Germany and the Netherlands. At weekends the café is popular with families. Ray has been the proprietor for nine years. He serves breakfasts and a full range of freshly prepared meals using local produce where possible. He has 100 per cent beef burgers with cheese, bacon and onions. Omelettes with various fillings and served with chips are from £2.10 as well as savoury pastries and gourmet sandwiches that can be eaten in the café or ordered by phone and delivered free of charge. If you're in a hurry, telephone your order first.

OPENING TIMES
Mon-Sat:	07.00 - 14.00
Sat:	07.00 - 12.00
Sun:	
Public holidays:	07.00 - 12.30

FACILITIES
Newspapers
Parking: cars/trucks: on street
Caravans/coaches: no

FOOD AND DRINK
Seating: 30
Daily specials
Kids' menu
Vegetarian menu
No alcoholic beverages

No credit cards

Sharon's Café

Nab Lane, Birstall WF17 9NG
Tel: 01924 475040

Directions: Exit the M62 at Junction 27 in the direction of Huddersfield. Turn left at the Pheasant Inn crossroads. Turn left down Nab Lane and go past the Volvo salesroom. Sharon's Café is further down that road on the left. It is five minutes from the M62. There is good entrance signage.

It is well worth the effort to find Sharon's Café, which is based in a bungalow. It may be small, with seats for only about 20, but the search is worthwhile. Sharon's hard work and bubbly personality over the last two years have rewarded her with a thriving business. Her home-cooked and freshly prepared meals are much enjoyed by truckers, whose yard is just next door. On her menu are the normal breakfasts, and also a special – breakfast in a flat cake, with sausage, bacon, eggs, beans, mushroom and toast at £3.45, served until 11.30 daily. Yorkshire puddings with a great selection of fillings range from £2.90 to £3.20. Spam was on the menu with various options which I hadn't seen anywhere else. 'Generous portions of delicious home cooking' was what one trucker told me!

Phone orders are welcome and can be delivered locally.

OPENING TIMES
Mon-Thu:	07.00 - 20.00
Fri:	07.00 - 14.30
Sat:	08.00 - 11.00
Sun; Public holidays:	Closed

FACILITIES
Newspapers
Parking: cars/trucks: plenty, in front of café entrance
Caravans/coaches welcome

FOOD AND DRINK
Seating: 19
Daily specials
Kids' menu
Vegetarian menu
No alcoholic beverages

No credit cards

The Six Hills Café

A46 Thrussington, Leicester LE7 4TF

Tel: 01507 588 424

Directions: Three and a half miles north of the roundabout A46/A607. Accessible northbound only - look out for the Total filling station - café is just behind it.

There has been a café on this site for many years and Penny, the present owner, has run it for about four. The café is not near any villages or houses and there are many people who take advantage of this. As Penny has noticed, it is common for people to use it as a meeting place for four cars, three of them left parked while they continue in one car, to shop in Nottingham – which can cause parking problems for truckers. .

Standard café fare is served, with much of the food being homemade. Typical daily specials are roast beef or pork with vegetables and gravy, or chicken casserole with vegetables or cottage pie. Prices start at around £3.70 with the most popular all-day breakfast at £3.50. Desserts include treacle sponge pudding and custard; apple pie and custard; rice pudding costing £1.50 each.

OPENING TIMES

Mon-Fri:	07.00 - 16.00
Sat:	07.30 - 12.00
Sun;	
Public holidays:	Closed

FACILITIES

Newspapers
Parking: cars: in front of café; trucks: in lay-by opposite

FOOD AND DRINK

Seating: 30
Daily specials
Kids' menu
Vegetarian menu
No alcoholic beverages

No credit cards

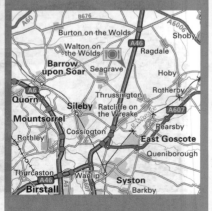

Standeford Farm Café

176 Stafford Road (A449), Standeford, Wolverhampton WV10 7BN

Tel: 01902 790389

Directions: Take Junction 12 of the M6 along the A5 towards Shrewsbury and take the A449 south. Alternatively, exit the M6 onto the M54. Then leave the M54 at Junction 2 for the A449. Standeford Farm Café is on the west side of the A449 and is well signposted.

Standeford Farm Café is a very convenient stopping place with plenty of 'off the road' truck and car parking. It's also used as a meeting place for businessmen.

The interior has recently undergone major refurbishment and redecoration, making a clean, efficient and busy café with friendly, welcoming staff.

The café serves a full range of meals. Breakfasts start at £4.00, with a mega or gammon breakfast at £4.50. There is a comprehensive menu of hot and cold snacks and a sandwich selection starting at £1.20. Main meals of mixed grills; lamb shanks or roast beef start at £4.70. Puddings include cheesecake and pies with custard or ice cream. On the first floor are showers and toilets, and a pleasant function room primarily for overnight drivers, with tables and chairs, TV, snooker table and fruit machines.

Opening Times

Mon-Thu:	05.30 - 20.00
Fri:	05.30 - 14.00
Sat-Sun;	
Public holidays:	Closed

Facilities

Disabled facilities
Washroom for drivers
Newspapers
Parking: cars: plenty; trucks: plenty, overnight £10.00 inc. free meal and shower
Caravans/coaches welcome

Food and Drink

Seating: 80
Daily specials
Kids' menu
Vegetarian menu
No alcoholic beverages

No credit cards

Stibbington Diner

2 Great North Road, Stibbington PE8 6LR
Tel: 01780 782891

Directions: At Stibbington on the A1, look for and follow the brown signs for the 'Nene Valley Railway'. Then follow signs for 'Services'. Well signposted on both north and south routes.

Close to the Nene Valley Railway Museum is the Stibbington Diner, a famous truckstop known to several generations of motorists. An example of the continuity of the Diner is Sid, who has been working the early morning shift for thirty years – not missing a day!

The café has a variety of customers including actors and film crews who regularly visit the café during filming of period railway scenes at the nearby museum – a sketch for *Trigger Happy TV* was shot here.

On the menu, dishes include roasts of the day £5.20; steak pie £4.30. All dishes are served with vegetables or salad and include tea or coffee. Desserts might be apple pie and custard £1.50; jam roly-poly £1.40; rice pudding £1.00, and ice cream £1.00. Owner Ian Taylor also supplies pizza takeaways, and will deliver. There's a separate bar area with Sky TV: open in the evenings.

OPENING TIMES
	24 hours
	06.00 Mon - 21.00 Sat
Sun:	08.00 - 21.00

FACILITIES
Washroom for drivers
Newspapers
Parking: cars: 40; trucks: 40, overnight £5.00 inc. free shower
Security: lighting, patrolled overnight
Caravans/coaches welcome

FOOD AND DRINK
Seating: 56
Daily specials
Kids' menu
Vegetarian menu
Alcoholic beverages (evenings)

No credit cards

The Stockyard Truckstop

J1 M18, Hellaby Industrial Estate, Hellaby, Rotherham S66 8HN
Tel: 01709 730083

Directions: From the M18, Junction 1, take A631 to Maltby. At the roundabout, turn left into Hellaby Industrial Estate. The truckstop is signed, but follow the road to the end of the estate, approximately one mile and The Stockyard is located at the end of the road.

This is a place that is full of surprises – an amazing truckstop, unique and much more sophisticated than you'd expect. Part of its attraction lies in the separate areas within it. Even the large restaurant is divided into small groupings. It serves steaks; pies; roast and vegetarian food, Sunday lunches being extremely popular.

Harry's Bar is a pub within the truckstop. The atmosphere is great, intimate, with olde worlde décor, and the added attraction of real ales being served.

Its construction using old beams and polished floorboards and use of antiques, gives the place a stylish look, which, coupled with the friendly staff under Mr Potts, makes for a very popular truckstop.

Opening times for the restaurant and café are different. The bar keeps to normal opening hours.

OPENING TIMES

Mon-Fri:	05.00 - 17.00
Sat:	06.00 - 14.00
Sun:	07.00 - 11.00
Public holidays:	open 08.00

FACILITIES

Disabled facilities
Washroom for drivers
Newspapers
Cash machine
Parking: cars: plenty; trucks: plenty, refrigerated spaces
Security: overnight
Caravans/coaches welcome

FOOD AND DRINK

Seating: 80
Outdoor eating area
Daily specials; Kids' menu
Vegetarian menu
Alcoholic beverages

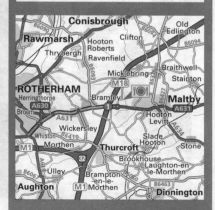

Sue's Pitstop Café

Unit 4A Ledston Luck Enterprise Park, Ridge Road, Kippax LS25 7BF
Tel: 0113 286 3307

Directions: From Junction 46 of the M1 take the A63 eastbound, or from Junction 47 of the M1 take the A656. After the crossroad of these two roads, Sue's Pitstop is south on the A656. At the time of writing there was no exterior sign. If you reach the turning for Kippax village you have gone too far.

Until 2004 the café was known as the Redwood Café. Sited on old pit premises and in a building that was originally the staff canteen, this popular stopping place was always referred to as the 'pitstop'. Sue took over the lease in January 2004 and the name change has evolved to Sue's Pitstop.

The team of staff are well known in the area and there is a lot of genuine banter and good-humoured teasing going on in the café. Basic café foods are served in good-sized portions that fully cover the plate.

The big English breakfasts are a favourite and constantly in demand all through the day. Daily roasts of beef, pork and turkey are at £4.20 each including three vegetables and Yorkshire pudding. Also specials, which include cottage pie, or chilli con carne with rice at £3.75.

OPENING TIMES

Mon-Fri:	07.00 - 15.00
Sat:	07.00 - 11.00
Sun;	
Public holidays:	Closed

FACILITIES

Newspapers
Parking: cars: plenty; trucks: plenty, refrigerated spaces, no overnight
Caravans/coaches welcome

FOOD AND DRINK

Seating: 56
Daily specials
Kids' menu
Vegetarian menu
No alcoholic beverages

No credit cards

Trigger's Café

Dunnington Lay-by, Hull Road, York YO19 5LP

Tel: 01904 481456

Directions: Set back on the lay-by on the north side of the A1079 about two miles from the York ring road, en route to Market Weighton and Beverley. Coming from the east, café is in lay-by behind very large brown tourist sign for York.

Dean Howson, the proprietor for the last 15 months, is happy to tell visitors how the name Trigger came about. He's commissioned a local artist to paint a mural on the wall with the story depicting Dean's time with the rugby fraternity and containing another clue – a link to *Only Fools and Horses!* You'll need to visit to find out what the association is …

The simple structure by the roadside has a clean and pleasant atmosphere and is popular with regular road users who frequently stop off to eat at the café. The food is the standard fare of truckers' fried breakfasts starting at £2.70 and going up to £3.40, which includes large mugs of coffee or tea. A full menu is available at sensible prices – specials include steak, peas and chips at £2.90 or 2 sausages, eggs and beans at £2.70, and vegetarian pasta dishes at £3.20.

OPENING TIMES

Mon-Sat:	06.00 - 17.00
Sun;	
Public holidays:	Closed

FACILITIES

Disabled facilities
Washroom for drivers
Newspapers
Parking: cars/trucks: in lay-by
Caravans: no
Coaches welcome
Garden
Children's play area

FOOD AND DRINK

Seating: 22
Outdoor eating area
Daily specials
Kids' menu
Vegetarian menu
No alcoholic beverages

No credit cards

Truckhaven

Scotland Road, Warton, Carnforth LA5 9RQ
Tel: 01524 736699

Directions: M6 near Carnforth, leave at Junction 35. Truckhaven is easy to find with large signage appearing about 12 miles before the junction. Follow the truckstop signs, turning left onto the A6. The truckstop is on the left.

A good and convenient stopping place that is clean, bright and well organised for truckers and car travellers, with plenty of parking. The very comfortable air-conditioned restaurant, with a separate area for smokers, offers breakfast with a choice of five items, served with tea or coffee and toast and butter at £4.50, plus a variety of home-cooked meals. There is a fresh roast every day, served with all the trimmings and costing £5.60.

Alternatively, if you are really hungry you can have an eight-item breakfast at £5.50. Also available: baked potatoes with a range of fillings; sandwiches and a help-yourself soup station where a portion of soup including roll and butter is £1.60 – excellent value. There is also a good selection of English puddings. Truckhaven also has a licensed sports bar, with a pool table, dartboard and large satellite TV screen. Live entertainment is sometimes put on in the lounge.

OPENING TIMES
Mon 05.30 - Sat 23.00
Sun: 07.00 - 23.00
Public holidays: 06.00 - 21.00

FACILITIES
Disabled facilities
Washroom for drivers
Newspapers, Cash machine
Parking: cars/trucks: plenty
Security: lighting, patrolled, CCTV, fenced
Caravans/coaches: no

ACCOMMODATION
Doubles: ensuite; TV: £40.00 (per room)
Singles: ensuite; TV: £30.00

FOOD AND DRINK
Seating: 120
Outdoor eating area
Daily specials; Kids' menu
Vegetarian menu
Alcoholic beverages (18.00–23.00, not Sundays)

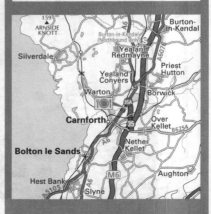

Truckstop Café

A19 Northbound, Exelby Filling Station, Ingelby Arncliffe, Northallerton DL6 3OG
Tel: 01609 882004

Directions: On the A19 northbound, about a mile after A684 to Northallerton, you will find the Exelby filling station. Truckstop Café is in the car park behind the station.

Well back from the fast main road and overlooking rolling countryside and fields, the café, owned by Janet Heal, is a pleasant, light and airy environment, with booth-style areas and large colourful potted plants.

On the menu you'll find a big all-day breakfast at £3.30 – one of the favourites. Another is the fish, chips, mushy peas and two slices of bread and butter at £3.95. Burgers and chips, sausages and mash also feature as daily popular meals.

The café is open everyday from 06.00 to 15.00 hours, but closes later at weekends and on public holidays, according to demand. Although there is not a designated play area, there is a large space for children to stretch their legs and run off some of their energy! With the big parking area alongside there is a truckstop run independently of the café.

OPENING TIMES

Mon-Fri:	06.00 - 15.00
Sat:	08.00 - 15.00
Sun;	
Public holidays:	07.00 - 15.00

FACILITIES

Disabled facilities
Washroom for drivers
Newspapers
Parking: cars/trucks: plenty
Caravans/coaches welcome

FOOD AND DRINK

Seating: 35
Outdoor eating area
Daily specials
Kids' menu
Vegetarian menu
No alcoholic beverages

No credit cards

Warley Cross Café

Beeford, Nr Brandesburton, Driffield YO25 8EW

Tel: 01262 488239

Directions: A165 from Hull to Bridlington, just north of dual carriageway in village of Beeford. Well signposted.

Jenny, the proprietor, and her team were thrilled to read the very complimentary write-up in the May 2005 issue of *Drive* – one that I can endorse.

Popular stop with drivers, families and children, the café serves generous helpings of daily homemade specials like stew with dumplings, chips and peas at £3.90 and lamb or beef with Yorkshire pudding at £3.90, plus a wonderful children's menu at £2.50 offering burgers, scampi and so on. Puddings include spotted dick; apple pie or fruit salad at £1.60. Breakfasts are a treat here, with the mega full-range variety at £4.50 to a more modest breakfast at £3.00. For those in a hurry, a takeaway favourite is the Belly Buster: a breakfast bun of egg, bacon, sausage, bean and tomato at £1.80.

A notice board has a list of local services available in the area.

OPENING TIMES
Mon-Sat: 07.30 - 14.00
Sun;
Public holidays: 08.00 - 14.00

FACILITIES
Disabled facilities
Newspapers
Parking: cars: 12; trucks: nearby
Caravans: welcome
Coaches: welcome, parking difficult

FOOD AND DRINK
Seating: 50
Daily specials
Kids' menu
Vegetarian menu
Alcoholic beverages

No credit cards

Way West Café

Great North Road, Darrington, Pontefract WF8 3HU

Tel: 0795 337 6847

Directions: Southbound on the A1 at the end of the present A1(M) construction at Ferrybridge. The Way West Café can't be missed. Or, come off the M62, southbound at Junction 35. It is half a mile down the A1 on your left.

When motorway works are completed the exterior and entrance of Way West will be improved, so don't be put off stopping here. Graham Reeves the proprietor, with his daughter Leanne, took over the business last year. They have already undertaken major refurbishment – the entrance offers a warm welcome, and the interior is now very pleasant with its blue banquettes around the edge of the room, and tables and chairs in the centre. There is a separate, raised, no-smoking area. Leanne offers all-day breakfasts from £3.40. Her main menu concentrates on hearty dishes of fish cakes or scampi, chips or salad, peas or beans at £4.00. Curries and steak and mushroom pie are some of the other dishes on offer around £4.00 – and a Canadian steak sandwich with chips and salad at £2.50. Puddings include crumbles and sponges all around £1.50. Homemade cakes and buns are also on sale.

OPENING TIMES

Mon-Fri:	07.00 - 18.00
Sat:	07.30 - 16.00
Sun:	09.00 - 16.00
Public holidays:	Closed

FACILITIES

Newspapers
Parking: cars/trucks: plenty
Caravans/coaches welcome

FOOD AND DRINK

Seating: 60
Daily specials
Kids' menu
No alcoholic beverages

No credit cards

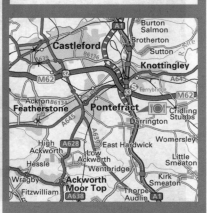

Welcome Sight Transport Café

6 Stafford Park, Stafford Park Industrial Estate, Telford TF3 3AT
Tel: 01952 293187

Directions: Leave M54 at Junction 4 and head for Telford. Turn into Stafford Park Industrial Estate at the Naird roundabout, marked by an obelisk. Follow road to area 6 and follow round to the right. Look for café on the left-hand side.

There has been a café in a prefabricated cabin on this site for about twenty years catering mainly for those working on the industrial estate. However it has become well known to truckers and other travellers because of the ample parking, both behind the café and along the road.

Owner Martin Wood has had the building enlarged and refurbished within the last year. The interior is now very smart – totally panelled in pine and sporting two oil paintings, painted by the mother of the lady who served me a mug of tea.

Standard café fare is all ordered off a board: breakfasts range from £3.05 to £4.55, which include re-fillable tea or coffee. Special was muffin burger (a muffin with a square sausage and egg) for £1.50.

The local area is famous for its connection with the Industrial Revolution. Thomas Telford's original 'Ironbridge' and the working Ironbridge Museum are nearby.

OPENING TIMES
Mon-Fri:	07.00 - 15.00
Sat:	07.00 - 13.00
Sun:	07.00 - 11.00
Public holidays:	Closed

FACILITIES
Newspapers: read only
Parking: cars: 20; trucks: 20
Caravans/coaches welcome

FOOD AND DRINK
Seating: 26
Vegetarian menu
No alcoholic beverages

No credit cards

Woodside Café

Rawcliffe Road, Airmyn, Goole DN14 8JU
Tel: 01405 839478

Directions: Leave M62 at Junction 36 (Goole) and take the A614 towards Rawcliffe. Café is about half a mile on right side. Well signposted. Set in open countryside and well lit.

The Dickinson family have run the Woodside Café for over 53 years and it is now with the third generation who have maintained the reputation for excellent food. Harry (the third), who began work here as a schoolboy, now runs the café.

Breakfast options start at £2.50 with the offer of extras of fried bread, fried potatoes, scrambled eggs, tomatoes, and mushrooms. Dripping sandwiches are 50p, and homemade pastries 55p. Puddings are from £1.10. Excellent value for money, with generous portions.

Good home-produced local fresh food is the motto – meats, sausages and vegetables are all from local farmers. Roast beef with Yorkshire pudding at £3.40; local ham, home baked with potatoes and vegetables, and braised liver with potatoes and vegetables are all around £3.35.

The large parking area has attracted not only truckers, but also a helicopter, and on one occasion, an elephant on a circus travel break!

OPENING TIMES
Mon-Thu:	06.15 - 17.00
Fri:	06.15 - 16.00
Sat-Sun;	
Public holidays:	Closed

FACILITIES
Disabled facilities
Newspapers
Parking: cars/trucks: plenty
Security: large secure park for truckers
Caravans/coaches welcome

FOOD AND DRINK
Seating: 60
Daily specials
Kids' menu
Vegetarian menu
No alcoholic beverages

No credit cards

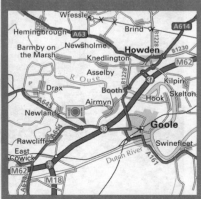

Woodside Café North

A19 Knayton (northbound), Thirsk YO7 4AJ
Tel: 01845 537077

Directions: On A19 northbound, about one mile north of Thirsk junction, set back in large truck park behind secluded lay-by – there is good signage for the café.

David Lofthouse's Woodside Café looks like Fort Knox due to the lonely location. The cabin has bars over the windows and doors, but once you enter you will see that recent refurbishment has taken place and the interior is far removed from first external impressions. A warm welcome and a large mug of tea is quickly forthcoming and large plates of all-day breakfasts then appear. There are lots of extras available as well, with prices starting at £2.85 up to £3.49. Fantastic value for money. On the board, the full menu contains a large variety of English foods: steak and kidney pie; braising steak; liver dishes. All of these include four types of vegetables with chips and cost from £3.75, or with mashed potato £3.90. The prices all seem very reasonable and the selection of English puddings look hearty and appetising.

For relaxation there's a wall-mounted TV.

OPENING TIMES
Mon-Fri:	06.00 - 22.00
Sat:	06.00 - 13.00
Sun;	
Public holidays:	Closed

FACILITIES
Washroom for drivers
Newspapers
Parking: cars: plenty; trucks: plenty, overnight £6.50 inc. meal voucher
Caravans welcome
Coaches: no
Garden
Children's play area

FOOD AND DRINK
Seating: 50
Daily specials
No alcoholic beverages

No credit cards

Woodside Café South A19

A19 Southbound, Knayton, Thirsk YO7 4AQ

Tel: 01845 537 459

Directions: Travelling southbound on the A19 from Middlesbrough, you will find the Woodside Café South is just before Thirsk turn off. There is a signpost before the entrance to the white building, set back from road.

New owner, Mrs Kathyrn Simpson is busy making significant improvements to this café both as regards the building and the food and ambience. Roadside cafés and truckstops were the topic of a recent TV documentary and featured the Woodside Café. The crew were impressed by the long hours and constant demand for good, hot homemade food throughout the day.

Breakfasts including bread and butter are £3.60–£3.95 with scrambled or fried eggs. Sandwiches are £1.35; egg, sausage and bacon £1.70. Specials include T-bone steak; toad-in-the-hole and chicken and mushroom pie from £3.95. Traditional puddings like crumble and hot chocolate fudge cake are £1.50. A set two-course dinner, freshly home cooked, at £4.95 is excellent value for money.

The restaurant is in one big pleasant room with a pool table at one end and a TV. A high chair is available for little ones.

OPENING TIMES
Mon-Thu: 06.30 - 20.00
Fri: 06.30 - 18.00
Sat-Sun;
Public holidays: Closed

FACILITIES
Newspapers
Parking: cars/trucks: plenty
Caravans welcome
Coaches: no

FOOD AND DRINK
Seating: 50
Daily specials
Kids' menu
No alcoholic beverages

No credit cards

Woodside Gardens and Tearooms

A314, Mundford Road, Cranwich IP26 5JN
Tel: 01842 878741

Directions: A134 Thetford to King's Lynn – village of Cranwich is after Mundford roundabout on right behind lay-by. Alternatively, travel the A1065 Newmarket to Fakenham, and at Mundford take A134 to Cranwich.

Mary and Bernard Rogers have opened their bungalow home to cater to passing drivers and visitors who are enjoying walks in the beautiful Thetford Forest Park, in which is the war memorial to the famous Desert Rats. Guests at Woodside Gardens can sample home cooking – whether it be an English breakfast with free-range eggs, or other homemade meals. Morning coffee is served with fresh coffee and biscuits and afternoon teas are served with homemade cakes. Lunches include cold and hot dishes. If you would like something later on, it would be advisable to telephone in advance, as the café closes at 18:30.

The bungalow has a very pretty English garden with plenty of flowers and blossoming fruit trees, at the end of a typical Norfolk village.

Close to the market towns of Downham Market and Swaffham, the area also has local vineyards to visit.

OPENING TIMES
Mon-Fri: 07.30 - 18.00
Sat-Sun:
Public holidays: Closed

FACILITIES
Parking: cars: 10;
trucks: in lay-by
Caravans/coaches: no
Garden

FOOD AND DRINK
Seating: 8
Outdoor eating area
No alcoholic beverages

No credit cards

188

Woodview Café

A1 North, Thornhaugh, Peterborough PE8 6HA
Tel: 01733 772030

Directions: Accessible northbound only. After passing the junction with the A47 (Peterborough) look for the sign to Thornhaugh. The café is a quarter of a mile further on, behind the service station.

The roadside café at Thornhaugh, now re-named Woodview, had been derelict for many years when Mrs Reid first saw it. It has now been totally refurbished and you can certainly detect a woman's touch – lace curtains, pictures and so on, making it a very comfortable and welcoming place to eat in. The café seats about sixty in the main area and around ten in a separate non-smoking room. Leeds United supporters will appreciate the memorabilia in this area.

All the food on the varied menu is home prepared and cooked to order with dishes like roast beef (medium £4.00, large £4.50); lasagne £4.00; mince and onion pie £4.00; chicken balti and rice £4.00, or chicken, chips and peas £4.00. Desserts include treacle sponge; jam roly-poly; spotted dick; fruit and ice cream; chocolate sponge £1.50. A light breakfast is £3.50, a cup of tea 50p and coffee 60p.

OPENING TIMES

Mon-Thu:	07.00 - 22.00
Fri:	07.00 - 17.00
Sat:	07.00 - 13.00
Sun:	
Public holidays:	Closed

FACILITIES

Newspapers: read only
Cash machine: in garage
Parking: cars: 20; trucks: 15, overnight £6.00 inc. £2.00 voucher
Caravans/coaches welcome

FOOD AND DRINK

Seating: 70
Outdoor eating area
Daily specials
Kids' menu
Vegetarian menu
No alcoholic beverages

No credit cards

189

Northern England and Scotland

This region includes the following counties:

Cumbria (part)	Ayrshire, South	Highland
County Durham	Ayrshire, North	Inverclyde
Northumberland	Borders (Scottish)	Lanarkshire, South
Tyne & Wear	City of Edinburgh	Lanarkshire, North
Yorkshire North (part)	City of Glasgow	Lothian, East
	Clackmannanshire	Lothian, West
Scotland	Dumfries & Galloway	Midlothian
Aberdeen City	Dunbartonshire, East	Moray
Aberdeenshire	Dunbartonshire, West	Perth & Kinross
Angus	Dundee City	Renfrewshire
Argyll & Bute	Falkirk	Renfrewshire, East
Ayrshire, East	Fife	Stirling

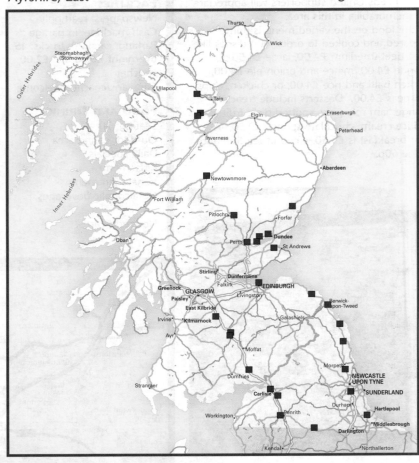

INDEX
Northern England and Scotland

Cedar Café

Grantshouse, Duns TD11 3RP
Tel: 01361 850371

Directions: On A1, north of Berwick-upon-Tweed, before the village of Grantshouse, set back on a lay-by. Well signposted.

The café is an attractive lodge-type of building with an outside covered veranda where on sunny days tables and chairs are put out. It is a quiet spot with wonderful walks up the hill behind the café or along by the river.

The café is always busy – at weekends families meet and eat here so it's a good idea to book in advance. Owner Keith Brown is welcoming to both his regulars and to new people passing though.

All-day breakfasts are on offer, the standard at £2.75 and the bumper at £4.75. Everything on the menu can be ordered at all times during the day. A local farm shop supplies all the meat, and the vegetables are sourced locally where possible.

Typical daily specials range between clam chowder or cock-a-leekie soup at £2.00, to a special roast chicken wrapped in bacon with haggis and pepper sauce for £6.50.

Toilets have recently been refurbished, and a separate internal shower unit installed.

OPENING TIMES

Mon-Fri:	08.00 - 20.00
Sat:	08.00 - 17.00
Sun;	
Public holidays:	08.00 - 20.00

FACILITIES

Disabled facilities
Washroom for drivers (separate)
Newspapers
Parking: cars: plenty; trucks: plenty in adjacent lay-by
Caravans/coaches welcome
Garden

FOOD AND DRINK

Seating: 52
Outdoor eating area
Daily specials
Kids' menu
Vegetarian menu
Alcoholic beverages

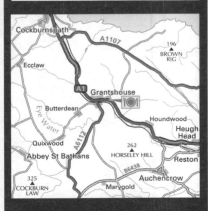

The Chef's Grill

Perth Road, Newtonmore, Scotland PH20 1BB
Tel: 01540 673702

Directions: The Chef's Grill is one mile from the A9 off the B9150 between Newtonmore and the A9. It is easier to access the café from the south via the B9150 to avoid Newtonmore and Kingussie. If coming from the north, come off the A9 at Kingussie and follow the loop road round to the B9150.

The staff at the Chef's Grill are friendly and welcoming – and who wouldn't be with such a fantastic view to look at all day: the café has large picture windows that look out over the snow-covered mountains. It is a popular starting point for walkers and many caravans overnight there as well.

The café is divided into two distinct smoking and non-smoking areas. The table service is efficient and owner John Hooper ensures the menu is enticing with specials such as giant Yorkshire pudding with a choice of fillings, Jamaican chicken salad, smoked haddock and poached egg or homemade stir fry, each for under £5.50. Desserts include lemon sponge or spotted dick with custard or ice cream.

For those wanting to spend a little longer, there is a pool table.

The Highland Information Centre is a little further down the road and there is also a petrol station and shop in the village.

OPENING TIMES

Mon-Fri:	06.30 - 22.00
Sat, Sun;	
Public holidays:	08.30 - 20.00
Xmas & New Year:	Closed

FACILITIES

Disabled facilities
Washroom for drivers
Newspapers
Parking: cars: plenty; trucks: plenty, £8.00 overnight
Caravans/coaches welcome

FOOD AND DRINK

Seating: 40
Outdoor eating area
Daily specials
Kids' menu
Vegetarian menu
Alcoholic beverages in bar

Clayton's Bistro Bar

Clayton Park, Cupar Road, St Andrews, Scotland KY16 9YB
Tel: 01334 871247
Directions: On the westbound side of the A91 between Cupar (6 miles) and St Andrews (5 miles).

It's easy to spot this bistro as it is in wide-open countryside and has flagpoles and a sweeping lawn leading up to it. It is also the entrance to a large caravan park behind it.

New manager, Robin Urquart, offers good food and over 40 dishes to choose from, including some unusually named ones like 'Hot Diggety' and 'Prince Charming', some Mediterranean dishes and some local Scottish foods – all good value at around £5.00.

At weekends they put on entertainment, making use of the raised stage and dance floor. Alcoholic drinks are available, including a good wine list. The bar, in an adjacent room, opens during normal licensing hours.

The bistro is child friendly with a menu designed especially for them, including high teas from three to seven o'clock and sandwiches and soup from five o'clock. There is also a large box of children's toys kept by the raised stage.

OPENING TIMES
Mon-Sun: 12.00 - 20.45

FACILITIES
Disabled facilities
Parking: cars/trucks: plenty
Caravans/coaches welcome
Garden
Children's play area

ACCOMMODATION
No accommodation, but a caravan park is attached.

FOOD AND DRINK
Seating: 90
Outdoor eating area
Daily specials
Kids' menu and high teas
Vegetarian menu
Alcoholic beverages

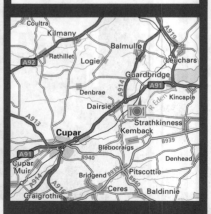

Crawford Arms Hotel

111 Carlisle Road, Crawford, Scotland ML12 6TP

Tel: 01864 502267

Directions: Leave the M74 between Glasgow and Carlisle at either Junction 14 (north or southbound) and take the A702 into the village of Crawford. The hotel is set on the east side of the road with parking opposite.

By the River Clyde and the dramatic Lanarkshire hills, in the village of Crawford, is the Crawford Arms Hotel and truckstop, recently acquired by Steven and Diane Porter. Many of the drivers who pass through the truckstop are enthusiastic football supporters, and the hotel bar often has a crowd around the TV. For those drivers wanting a more peaceful stopover at the end of the day, the owners have created a comfortable quiet corner for relaxation. There is also a pool room.

All-day breakfasts at £4.00, plus a comprehensive menu of traditional fare are available: soups at £2.00 and main courses around £5.00 are typical with puddings like jam roly-poly at £2.50. Truckers can park for £10 per night, which includes a three-course evening meal.

The accommodation in the hotel has been simply refurbished quite recently. The cost is £29.00 per person, which includes breakfast and an evening meal.

OPENING TIMES

Mon-Fri:	06.00 - 20.00
Sat-Sun;	
Public holidays:	08.00 - 20.30

FACILITIES

Washroom for drivers
Newspapers
Parking: cars/trucks: plenty, overnight £10 inc. evening meal
Caravans/coaches welcome

ACCOMMODATION

3 Doubles; 4 Family;
1 Single

FOOD AND DRINK

Seating: 40
Outdoor eating area
Daily specials; Kids' menu
Vegetarian menu
Alcoholic beverages in bar
(11.00–23.00)

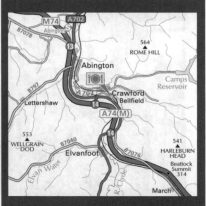

Europa Truckstop

Wellburn Interchange, Carlisle Road, Lesmahagow, Scotland ML11 0HY

Tel: 01555 894889 email: manio@europatruckstop.com www.europatruckstop.com
Directions: On M74 at Junction 9 southbound or Junction 10 northbound.

This truckstop has recently undergone tremendous refurbishment and has plenty to offer to all road users. The reception area even has a barber's chair, in use on Thursdays. There is also a shop, selling everyday necessities for the driver, right down to drivers' work clothes. The shop is close to the CCTV control counter.

In the large canteen with a carvery counter, you can get breakfasts with eggs cooked every way you can think of, plus the usual roasts, grills and pastas all around £5.00 or less, and puddings like crumbles or rice pudding. A complete meal of a main course including vegetables and potatoes and a pudding costs £5.95.

The truckstop has accommodation and also a licensed bar with a small seating area, and a larger space, decorated with musical instruments, with dance floor, stage and a DJ room. Proprietor, Manio Loia, encourages evening events and promotes young talented artists. This pleasant room is also available for private functions and events.

OPENING TIMES

Mon-Thu:	05.00 - 23.00
Fri:	05.00 - 22.00
Sat:	06.00 - 16.00
Sun;	
Public holidays:	09.00 - 22.30

FACILITIES

Disabled facilities
24-hour washroom for drivers
Newspapers
Parking: cars/trucks: plenty
Security: CCTV/fenced area for trucks, 24-hour CTV
Caravans/coaches welcome

ACCOMMODATION

11 Doubles: ensuite; TV: single occupancy £15; double occupancy £25.50

FOOD AND DRINK

Seating number: 70
Daily specials; Kids' menu
Vegetarian menuAlcoholic beverages in bar (11.00–23.00)

196

The Horn Restaurant

A90, Errol, Perth, Scotland PH2 7SR
Tel: 01821 670237

Directions: 11 miles from Dundee/11 miles from Perth. On the A90 Dundee to Perth road, on south side of road. Well signposted.

The Horn Restaurant is easy to spot, as above the restaurant at roof level is a full-sized black and white cow.

Owner Kenny Farquharson has run the business since 1959. It's a popular stopping place for drivers and their families, as well as coaches, all getting a genuine welcome from the staff. Coach drivers should phone in about half an hour before they arrive to ensure hot food is ready for their arrival.

In the entrance you'll find a small shopping area selling jams, honeys, biscuits and other locally manufactured food and Scottish gift products. There is also an ice cream counter with a good selection to choose from.

The restaurant operates a counter service. Most of the dishes are homemade and include lasagne; roasts, and shepherds pie from £6.70 to £8.00. A good selection of vegetables and potatoes are also available plus a selection of salads and fresh raw vegetables.

If kids don't want a whole meal, they can have their own lunch box put together, which includes a variety of healthy snacks and foods, plus a drink. Anything they don't eat in the restaurant can be taken away with them for their onward journey – a popular idea.

OPENING TIMES
Mon-Sun: 08.30 - 17.00
Public holidays: 09.00 - 17.00

FACILITIES
Disabled facilities
Newspapers
Parking: cars/trucks: plenty
Caravans/coaches welcome

FOOD AND DRINK
Seating: 84
Daily specials
Kids' menu
Vegetarian menu
Alcoholic beverages

Horseshoe Café

Abernyte Road, Inchture, Perth, Scotland PH14 9RS
Tel: 01828 686283
Directions: From Dundee to Perth on A90, Horseshoe Café is on the north side. Take Inchture turn off up to Abernyte Road. Easy to see on hillside, set back off new road, by new flyover.

The café has a large car park in front of it, and the building is decorated with horseshoes, the theme being continued inside with a number of framed pictures of horses, farm livestock, tractors and so on.

Owner Mike Burns is an ex-truck driver. With his daughter Jane, who does the cooking, and other members of his family working alongside them, they are all involved in the running of the café, so it is very much a family affair.

Good hearty breakfasts with black pudding are on the menu – if you don't like black pudding, you can choose something else – at £4.00 including tea or coffee.

Specials such as steak pie, or breaded haddock include vegetables and potatoes and cost £4.50. A good-looking sirloin steak costs £8.50.

There is a patio with wonderful views over the Sidlaw Hills, and in the summer it's an outdoor eating area.

OPENING TIMES

Mon-Fri:	08.00 - 21.00
Sat:	08.00 - 15.00
Sun:	09.30 - 19.00
Public holidays:	Closed

FACILITIES

Disabled facilities
Washroom for drivers
Newspapers
Parking: cars/trucks: plenty
Caravans/coaches welcome

FOOD AND DRINK

Seating: 84
Outdoor eating area
Daily specials
Vegetarian menu
No alcoholic beverages

No credit cards

Hungry Trucker Café

20 Carlisle Road, Crawford, Scotland ML12 6TW

Tel: 01864 504227   Email: phil@heatherghyll.co.uk

Directions: Leave the M74 at either Junction 14 (north or southbound), between Glasgow and Carlisle. Hotel and Café is on the left before village.

This small country hotel with a truckstop café is in beautiful Upper Tweeddale. The Hungry Trucker park is next to the hotel, overlooking the river and the magical Scottish hills on the Clyde Valley tourist route.

Owned by Phil Leek, the hotel is popular with travellers and has a cosy bar with a wood-burning stove, comfy leather chairs and a TV and is decorated with walking sticks and pictures of highland sheep.

Truckers and guests share the same functional dining room and another café-style room, with bright yellow walls, and a big TV. Food is prepared all day, closing at 21.00 (an hour earlier in winter).

Main meals include haggis (of course); omelettes or haddock dishes at £3.80, with a choice of starters from £1.90. Breakfasts are standard at £3.50, or substantial – the trucker's breakfast is £4.30.

A children's menu starting at £2.60 includes nuggets, lasagne and fish fingers.

OPENING TIMES

Mon-Fri:	06.00 - 21.00
Sat:	07.00 - 21.00
Sun:	12.00 - 21.00
Public holidays:	Closed

FACILITIES

Disabled facilities
Parking: cars/trucks: plenty
Caravans/coaches welcome

ACCOMMODATION

5 bedrooms: ensuite; TV, breakfast included in price.

FOOD AND DRINK

Seating: 60
Daily specials
Kids' menu
Vegetarian menu
Alcoholic beverages in bar

No credit cards

Lady Ross

The Main Street, Ardgay, Bonar Bridge, Sutherland, Scotland IV24 3DH
Tel: 01863 766315

Directions: From the A9, take the A836 towards Bonar Bridge. Ardgay is some 15 miles along the road. It is well signposted before, and on entering the village. On entering the village you will find the café on the left, just after the war memorial.

The centrepiece of the pretty village of Ardgay, at the top end of Dornoch Firth, the Lady Ross combines a café, a lounge and bar as well as the village post office that sells a few basic supplies.

The café is now owned by Colin Mitchell, whose staff are very helpful and efficiently serve up anything from sandwiches and toasties at around £2.00 to homemade lasagne for £5.70 or a mini grill (burger, egg, bacon, sausage, beans and black pudding) for £6.55 – all good value.

The café is very busy during the summer with tourists visiting Balblair Forest and the Achness Waterfalls. It is also used regularly by the locals, who make extensive use of the café's takeaway service.

The inside of the café is a bit dark, but is cheerfully decorated with bright blue tablecloths. In the lounge is a pool table and a dartboard.

There is a petrol station nearby.

OPENING TIMES
Mon-Sun; Public holidays:
10.00 - 20.00
(not Xmas & New Year)

FACILITIES
Cash machine in post office
Parking: cars: plenty; trucks: plenty, need permission to park overnight
Caravans welcome
Small coaches welcome

FOOD AND DRINK
Seating: 60
Daily specials
Kids' menu
Vegetarian menu
Alcoholic beverages

No credit cards

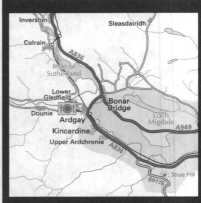

Last Drop Café

Smeaton Road, West Gourdie Industrial Estate, Dundee, Scotland DD2 4UT

Tel: 01382 621941

Directions: Follow sign for the truckstop around the A90 Dundee bypass.
The West Gourdie Industrial Estate is between the A90 Perth and A923 Blairgowrie.
The Last Drop Café is adjacent to the truckstop.

The Last Drop Café is adjacent to the truck park so it goes without saying that a great many of the regulars are truck drivers, but it also has a large local customer base.
Run by the Wilkie family, the café opens from around 07.00 until 21.00 hours every day of the week – it is always full, one reason being that it would be difficult to improve on the quality of the food, which includes all-day breakfasts and many daily specials.
The licensed bar has a pleasant seating area, part of it in booths if you want some privacy, and there is also an area set aside for families. In a separate room is a pool table and darts board. This room is also used for private family events and parties.

Opening Times

Mon:	07.00 - 21.00
Tue-Fri:	06.30 - 21.00
Sat:	07.30 - 12.00
Sun; Public holidays:	Closed

Facilities

Disabled facilities
Washroom for drivers
Newspapers; Cash machine
Parking: cars/trucks: plenty
Security: CCTV
Caravans/coaches welcome

Food and Drink

Seating: 40
Outdoor eating area
Daily specials; Kids' menu
Vegetarian menu
Alcoholic beverages

No credit cards

The Lorry Park Café

Good Station Road, Lockerbie, Scotland DG11 2HA
Tel: 07751 297540

Directions: Leave A74(M) at Junction 17 or Junction 18 and follow sign to Lockerbie Town Centre. There is signage to the truckstop. The Lorry Park Café is up street between the Post Office and Police Station, and near Somerfield's car park.

Converted two years ago into a café with lorry park, The Lorry Park Café is in the centre of town. Trucks are signposted into town on a special route so that they don't disrupt the town's traffic system.

Located between the Post Office, Police Station and the car park of Somerfield supermarket, this café is used by truck drivers, tourists to Lockerbie and area, and other members of the public. It opens for business at 06.00 and remains busy all day.

The simplicity of the inside of the café is a good background for showing off the café's private collection of about 80 model classic trucks, which are painted in the company colours and logos that we all recognise from driving along the motorways.

All-day breakfasts are about £4.60; plates of ham salad, or roast beef and salad, and chicken curry are in the region of £4.00. Puddings of jam roly-poly or treacle sponge with custard are £1.50. Hot rolls of haggis or hash browns are £1.50.

The proprietor, Fiona, and her husband Peter, obviously enjoy the challenge of running a busy café.

Opening Times

Mon-Thu:	06.00 - 22.00
Fri:	06.00 - 20.00
Sat:	08.00 - 15.00
Sun; Public holidays:	Closed

Facilities

Disabled facilities
Washroom for drivers
Telephone (outside)
Newspapers
Parking: cars/trucks: plenty
Caravans/coaches welcome

Accommodation

None on site, but manager can arrange nearby

Food and Drink

Seating for 50
Daily specials; Kids' menu
Vegetarian menu
No alcoholic beverages

No credit cards

Market Buffet

3 Pier Place, Edinburgh, Scotland EH6 4LP
Tel: 0131 478 7678

Directions: Coastal road, Edinburgh to Forth Bridge. Take A901 from Leith Docks to Newhaven. Market Buffet is directly opposite the harbour and the Inchcolm Ferry.

Opposite the pretty Scottish quay at Newhaven you'll find Joyce Thompson's tiny and delightful café. Open from 05.00 weekdays and 08.00 Sundays, it's very popular and well used by the fishermen from the fleet that comes into this small seaport – currently undergoing some redevelopment.

On the day of our visit, the café was full of colourful locals, as well as truckers passing through Edinburgh. The banter was fun and genuine, as great plates of homemade shortcake and rock buns were washed down with large mugs of tea and coffee.

Large plates of breakfasts are on offer priced at £3.20 and breakfast phone orders are welcomed.

The café has a window that opens out onto the street and during the summer, you can buy tickets here for the Maid of Forth–Incholm Ferry, as well as getting ice creams and ice lollies.

OPENING TIMES
Mon-Fri:	05.00 - 12.00
Sun:	08.00 - 11.00
Sat; Public holidays:	Closed

FACILITIES
Newspapers
Parking: cars/trucks: on street

FOOD AND DRINK
Seating: 40

No credit cards

Moorhouse Farm

21 Station Road, Stannington Station, Morpeth NE61 6DX
Tel: 01670 789016

Directions: A1 from Newcastle to Morpeth. Take the exit for Stannington Station and Hepscott (old A1) and follow sign for Service Station. First right is Station Road. Moorhouse Farm is down this road on the left-hand side.

Well worth a stop off the main road, where farm barns have been converted into a farm shop and restaurant selling Northumbrian produce and home-reared beef, lamb and pork from the Byatt's farm, as well as preserves, cheeses and fruit and veg. The farmhouse restaurant serves delicious homemade soups with locally made breads for £2.95, as well as traditional main courses like hot beef 'stottie' with onions, mushrooms and gravy in a bun with potato crisps for £3.45, also quiches and puddings, cakes and patisserie, and local wines. Staff are friendly and obviously enjoy the pleasant environment. This is a busy place, popular with locals and those who make the detour off the A1. Moorhouse Farm is a member of the Northumbrian Larder, and the Certified Farmers' Market.

OPENING TIMES

Tue-Sat: 09.30 - 17.30
Sun: 10.00 - 16.00
Mon; Public holidays: Closed

FACILITIES

Disabled facilities
Parking: cars: plenty; trucks: nearby
Caravans: yes; coaches: advance notice required
Garden

FOOD AND DRINK

Seating: 60
Outdoor eating area
Daily specials
Vegetarian menu
Alcoholic beverages

The Motorgrill

Old A90, Ballinluig, Pitlochry, Scotland PH9 0LG
Tel: 01796 482212

Directions: The Motorgrill is at the junction of the A9 and A827. It is well signed off the A9. On entering the village, turn left at the T-junction and the café is located along the road on the right. There is a petrol station next door.

The Motorgrill is located in a beautiful setting and is close to many tourist attractions including Dunkeld and the shopping experience of The House of Bruar.

Table service at the café is very efficient with plenty of staff on hand, so no one has to wait long to be served. The café is clean and airy and is obviously very popular with locals as well as those travelling through.

The Motorgrill has a big menu. All the specials are homemade and where possible the ingredients are sourced locally, like the Scottish scampi, which comes with chips and peas for £6.25, with dessert to follow of perhaps blackcurrant and apple pie and ice cream for £2.55.

All main courses on the kids' menu are priced at £2.20 and desserts are 99p. High chairs are available.

Outside there's an attractive patio with tables and chairs where you can sit and make the most of the lovely surroundings. Wheelchair access is very easy.

The restaurant is owned by Clive Bridges.

OPENING TIMES
Mon-Sun: 08.00 - 20.30
Public holidays: 08.00 - 20.30
(not Xmas & New Year)

FACILITIES
Disabled facilities
Washroom for drivers
Newspapers, at garage
Parking: cars/trucks: plenty
Caravans/coaches welcome

ACCOMMODATION
No accommodation on site, but at pub next door

FOOD AND DRINK
Seating: 56
Outdoor eating area
Daily specials (not weekends)
Kids' menu
Vegetarian menu
No alcoholic beverages

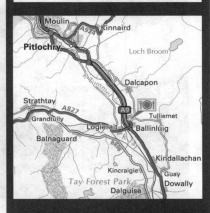

Nancy's Harbour Restaurant

Shore Road, Perth, Scotland PH2 8BD
Tel: 01738 625788
Directions: Leave M90 at Junction 11 (or M90 Junction 10).
Bridge of Earn – down to Docks. Nancy's is at Port entrance gates.

Down by the harbour wall, close to the entrance gate to the Dockyard, you will see a freshly painted sign telling you it is Nancy's Harbour Restaurant and Bed and Breakfast. Since the Watsons bought the restaurant three years ago they have refurbished the restaurant, now decorated in blue, cream and white colours, and on the walls, wonderful old black and white prints of the harbour and dock area.

Word is going about that the breakfasts at Nancy's are some of the best in Perth so the restaurant is popular among the locals (confirmed by the local policeman!). Other dishes looked extremely appetising including Scottish scampi at £4.95, and breaded North Sea haddock at £4.65, all locally supplied. The cakes are made locally in Falkirk, and are quite delicious.

Accommodation consists of seven pleasantly decorated bedrooms, all ensuite with TV. Bed and breakfast from £25.00. The business operates a no-smoking policy throughout.

OPENING TIMES
Mon-Thu:	06.30 - 18.00
Fri:	06.30 - 16.00
Sat:	08.00 - 13.00
Sun; Public holidays:	Closed

FACILITIES
Disabled facilities
Washroom for drivers
Newspapers
Parking: cars/trucks: plenty
Caravans/coaches welcome

ACCOMMODATION
3 Double: ensuite, TV:
£40 b&b
4 Single: ensuite, TV:
£25 b&b

FOOD AND DRINK
Seating: 44
Daily specials; Kids' menu
Vegetarian menu
No alcoholic beverages

NT Truckstop

Portobello Road, Birtley DH3 2SN
Tel: 0191 492 0940

Directions: A1/A194(M) junction, exit Junction 65 and follow sign to NT Truckstop.

This restaurant/motel and truckstop, managed by Denise Fallows, is used by locals and truckers alike. The truckstop has a useful in-house shop selling milk and newspapers, and there's a 24-hour canteen and restaurant as well.

The restaurant is light, airy, with a long serving counter. On the menu are the standard English breakfasts, plus other dishes like Cajun chicken at £5.75 or Cumberland sausages at £4.99. Potatoes and other veg are included in the price. Burgers also feature, as does a long list of puddings and ice creams. Fresh coffee and designer teas are served in a bottomless cup! – you can top up free for 99p.

As well as accommodation, there's a small quiet TV room and next to it, the licensed bar (open normal licensing hours) with a big TV screen showing mostly SKY sports programmes. Can be noisy at times! There's also a dartboard and pool table.

OPENING TIMES
Mon-Fri: 24 hours
06.00 Mon - 12.00 Sat
12.00 Sat & Sun: Closed

FACILITIES
Disabled facilities
Washroom for drivers
Newspapers; Cash machine
Parking: cars/trucks: plenty
Security: CCTV/fenced area for trucks
Caravans/coaches welcome

ACCOMMODATION
Motel: 4 Double: £25.50
5 Single: £14.99

FOOD AND DRINK
Daily specials
Kids' menu
Vegetarian menu
Alcoholic beverages in bar

NT Truckstop

Kingstown Trading Estate, Parkhouse Road, Carlisle CA3 0JR

Tel: 01228 534192   Fax: 01228 515508

Directions: Travelling along the A74 north of Carlisle, come off at Junction 44. At the roundabout, take A7 to town centre. At the first set of traffic lights turn right and follow the road to the end. Nightowl is on the left before you reach Asda.

NT Truckstop is a typical modern truckstop, which, importantly for truckers, has a large secure parking area for overnight stops. It's also a useful stopping place for other road users.

The food here is really good, with daily specials and delicious breakfast fare. All prices range between £4 and £5. Pasta dishes, stews and curries are some of the menu choices.

The coffee and tea is good and refills are free while you remain in the restaurant.

The restaurant is light and airy, with a reception area for drivers, and a shop selling basic travellers' necessities. The lounge is comfortable and has a licensed bar as well as a large TV screen, pool table and darts board. Drivers can expect high standards. The showers are great and accommodation is available with 40 rooms, including 5 doubles with ensuite facilities.

Welcoming staff are managed by Supervisor, Sandra.

OPENING TIMES
Mon-Sun: 24 hours

FACILITIES
Disabled facilities
Washroom for drivers
Newspapers
Cash machine
Parking: cars/trucks: plenty
Security: CCTV/fenced area for trucks
Caravans/coaches welcome

ACCOMODATION
5 Double: ensuite; 16 Twin
18 Single: £17.99
Secure entry

FOOD AND DRINK
Seating: 84
Daily specials
Vegetarian menu
Alcoholic beverages in bar

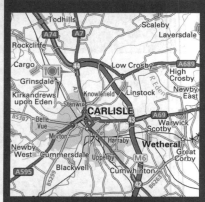

Penrith Truckstop

Haweswater Road, Penrith Industrial Estate, Penrith CA11 9EH
Tel: 01768 866995

Directions: Exit the M6 at Junction 40 and follow the signs into Penrith. At the intersection with the A66 follow signs to the town centre. At the mini roundabout, go left and follow the signs to the truckstop – along the road on the left opposite BOCM.

It's well worth a five-minute detour off the motorway to find this well-run truckstop owned by Alan Jenkinson, where the staff are cheery and friendly and the overall atmosphere really welcoming.

There's plenty of car parking around the building, plus well-maintained gardens that the customers appreciate.

The restaurant seats 100 and is very practical. All-day breakfast menus start at £3.20 through to £5.60, while other meals in the £5.00 range might include mince and dumpling or chicken and leek pie, all served with vegetables and potatoes and good value for money.

Upstairs is a pleasant, modernized lounge with leather chairs, TV and a small stage, bar and dance floor. This connects with another room that is used for seminars and meetings.

OPENING TIMES
Mon-Sat:	06.00 - 13.30
Sun:	12.00 - 21.30
Public holidays:	Closed

FACILITIES
Disabled facilities
Washroom for drivers
Newspapers, Cash machine
Parking: cars/trucks: plenty
Security: CCTV/fenced area for trucks
Caravans/coaches welcome

ACCOMMODATION
1 Single: £20
Secure entry

FOOD AND DRINK
Seating: 100
Daily specials; Kids' menu
Vegetarian menu
Alcoholic beverages in bar

No credit cards

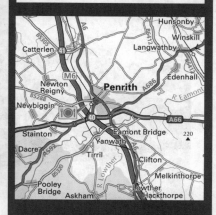

Purdy Lodge Café

Adderstone Services, Belford NE70 7JU
Tel: 01668 213000 Fax: 01668 213131 www.purdylodge.co.uk
Directions: On the A1 junction with the B1341 to Bamburgh Castle and close to
Chillingham Castle. Between Alnwick and Berwick-upon-Tweed.

Owned by the Purdy Lodge, an independent family company, this purpose-built, modern café is very popular with travellers, families and tourists on the A1 north/south road. It has plenty of facilities including a restaurant, sporting bar and a café.

The café itself is open all day. It is within the lodge complex and has its own entrance and facilities. The fast canteen service offers a range of fried and grilled meals, as well as salads, sandwiches, baked potatoes and omelettes – average price £5.00.

In the café you can buy locally made gifts; things for the journey, and a variety of groceries for the holiday cottages that are scattered throughout this beautiful countryside. Outside the entrance to the café is an old hand-held farm plough, and a red telephone kiosk.

Nearby is the 24-hour Adderstone Service Station, which, in addition to a full range of fuel, including LPG, has a well-stocked convenience store and houses a Tourist Information Centre. Additional bonus – a mechanic is on hand in case of breakdowns!

Opening Times
Mon-Sun: 24 hours

Facilities
Disabled, Newspapers
Parking; cars: 20; trucks: 40
Caravans/coaches welcome
Garden
Children's play area

Accommodation
Double: ensuite; TV; Tel
Twin: ensuite; TV; Tel
Single: ensuite; TV; Tel
Family: ensuite; TV; Tel
Secure entry

Food and Drink
Seating: 60
Daily specials
Kids' menu
Vegetarian menu
Alcoholic beverages in bar

Riverside Café

7 Main Street, Tweedmouth, Berwick-upon-Tweed TD15 2AA
Tel: 01289 303227

Directions: From A1 take Berwick Bypass and enter Tweedmouth on the A1167. Look out for signs to the harbour. Riverside Café is on the main street before the harbour.

This charming French-style café is almost under the amazing bridge over the River Tweed and close to the old one-way traffic bridge from Berwick. It has two very large sash windows onto the quiet main street and it looks very inviting, with high ceilings and large black and white prints on the wall. Popular with locals and visitors, it attracts many people in for a good meal. At weekends you may have to queue for a table.

Sunday mornings are busy, with full English breakfasts being served. Seating only about 24, the café operates on a first-come, first-served basis.

Breakfasts are a big favourite, and people can order takeaways. Amongst other favourites are the roasts and curries for around £4.50. Proprietor Alison Ainslie prepares and cooks daily specials every morning and she also makes a point of preparing an especially good kids' menu featuring all their favourite dishes. There is a high chair.

OPENING TIMES

Mon-Fri:	09.00 - 21.00
Sat:	09.00 - 15.00
Sun;	
Public holidays:	10.00 - 15.00

FACILITIES

Parking: cars: street parking in front of café; trucks: plenty in harbour area nearby
Caravans/coaches welcome

FOOD AND DRINK

Seating: 24
Daily specials
Kids' menu
Vegetarian menu
No alcoholic beverages

No credit cards

Skiach Services

Evanton Industrial Estate, Evanton, Scotland IV16 9XJ

Tel: 01349 830888

Directions: Skiach Services is 25 miles north of Inverness. The café is 50 yards off the A9 on the B9176 at the side of the Evanton Industrial Estate. The services are well signed off the main road.

The café, managed by Paul Martin, is often used by truckers and gives a good service including a bar in a separate room, gaming machines and a pool table. The menu offers the normal trucker's fare: all-day breakfasts, and specials like green pea soup at £1.90, roast lamb and three vegetables at £4.95 and raspberry Pavlova at £1.90. Orders are placed at the service counter and the food is delivered efficiently to waiting customers. There is a good children's play area with a slide and play equipment shaped like a boat – ideal for children who have been cooped up in a car for a long time. Parents are able to sit outside and enjoy a drink or their meal while keeping an eye on their children playing. There is a 24-hour filling station on the same site.

OPENING TIMES

Mon-Fri:	07.00 - 22.00
Sat:	07.00 - 20.00
Sun:	08.00 - 20.00
Public holidays	07.00 - 22.00

(not Xmas & New Year)

FACILITIES

Disabled facilities
Washroom for drivers
Newspapers
Cash machine at filling station
Parking: cars: plenty; trucks: plenty
Caravans/coaches welcome
Children's play area

FOOD AND DRINK

Seating: 100
Outdoor eating area
Daily specials; Kids' menu
Vegetarian menu
Alcoholic beverages at bar

Stainmore Café

A66 at Brough CA17 4EU

Directions: Travelling along the A66, five miles east of Brough, between Scotch Corner and Penrith. While it is possible to access the café from both directions, drivers should be very careful, as some drivers go at great speed on this stretch of road.

Dramatic views of the Lune Forest can be seen from Stainmore Café. With plenty of parking for cars and trucks, this simple but popular café caters for all travellers and truck drivers. Seating is along red bar counters, with bar stools placed to make the most of the magnificent views out of the windows over the fells. In summer, customers can eat outside at tables placed behind the shelter of a stone wall.

Owner Mark Laib's menu is unpretentious, but the food is well prepared and enticing. Main items on the menu include sirloin steak with chips, peas, onion rings, plus tea or coffee, at £5.95 and large breakfasts at £4.00, with extras like mushrooms at about 30p per item – one could feast on this alone. They also serve chip butties that look really great, loaded with fresh fried chips and smelling very appetising – at £1.30 a bargain.

OPENING TIMES

Mon-Thu:	06.00 - 20.00
Fri:	06.00 - 19.00
Sat:	06.00 - 16.00
Sun;	
Public holidays:	07.00 - 19.00

FACILITIES

Disabled facilities
Newspapers
Parking: cars/trucks: plenty
Caravans/coaches welcome

FOOD AND DRINK

Seating: 25
Outdoor eating area
Daily specials
Kids' menu
Vegetarian menu
No alcoholic beverages

No credit cards

The Storehouse Restaurant and Farmshop

A9 Evanton, Scotland IV16 9UX
Tel: 01349 830038

Directions: North of Inverness, just off the A9 before Evanton and adjacent to the Cromarty Firth. The Storehouse is well signposted.

The Storehouse Restaurant is in a beautiful old building and the views from the window are breathtaking. However, there is much more on offer at this thriving business, which was taken over by local farmer Quentin Stevens and Andrew and Fiona MacInnes in 2005. The restaurant staff are welcoming and helpful and the menu is enticing. Everything is home cooked and locally sourced where possible and one customer was heard to remark on how delicious the roast chicken was and what a pleasant surprise it was to see it being carved from the bird just before serving. Other items on the menu included quiches, pies, salads and breads.

In a separate area you will find comfortable chairs and newspapers. There is also a well-stocked farm shop with local meats and breads amongst the items on sale.

OPENING TIMES

Mon-Sat: 09.00 - 19.00
                  (18.00 in Winter)
Sun;
Public holidays: 10.00 - 17.00
                  (not Xmas & New Year)

FACILITIES

Disabled facilities
Newspapers
Parking: cars: plenty;
trucks: none
Caravans: welcome
Coaches: advance notice required
Garden; Children's play area

FOOD AND DRINK

Seating: 75
Outdoor eating area
Daily specials
Kids: small portions of mains
Vegetarian menu
Alcoholic beverages

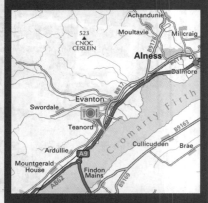

Stracathro Services

A90, Stracathro, Brechin, Scotland DD9 7PX

Tel: 01674 840 236

Directions: On the A90 northbound, three miles north of Brechin. Well signed off road. For access going south, come off A90 and go over bridge, also well signed.

Stracathro Services is a large, airy restaurant with helpful and cheerful staff. The restaurant is divided into two separate areas for smoking and non-smoking, the latter being more comfortable than the former. There's a shop on the premises selling everyday items and local produce such as honey and eggs. Although the exterior of the restaurant is not all that inviting, you'll be pleased with the reasonable prices and friendly atmosphere. There is an extensive menu, much of which is home cooked and where possible, locally sourced. Portions are generous and might include pork casserole at £5.40 followed by strawberry crumble and ice cream for £1.30. Many locals support the café and there are a lot of loyal regulars who enjoy a good laugh with the staff.

The restaurant is owned by Transis Ltd and managed by Pat Melville Evans.

OPENING TIMES

Mon-Fri:	06.00 - 21.00
Sat:	06.00 - 20.00
Sun:	07.00 - 21.00
Public holidays:	06.00 - 21.00

(not Xmas & New Year)

FACILITIES

Disabled facilities
Washroom for drivers
Newspapers
Cash machine in garage.
Parking: cars: plenty; trucks: plenty, overnight £7.50 inc. meal voucher.
Caravans/coaches welcome

FOOD AND DRINK

Seating: 100
Daily specials
Kids' menu
Vegetarian menu
No alcoholic beverages

Thistle Café

Golden Fleece Services, Carleton, Carlisle CA4 0AN
Tel: 07734 701637

Directions: Leave M6 at Junction 42. The café can be reached through truckstop at BP station, or off the A6.

The café is in a converted house next to the Golden Fleece BP station.

The views over the Cumbrian countryside are terrific. Owner Margaret MacGilivray has been overseeing this family run business for about fourteen years and two years ago Alison joined forces with Margaret. Alison's sparky personality and genuine joie de vivre make sure everyone has a good laugh and feels at home.

The café is nicely decorated and the ground floor turned into one large room, with a serving counter in front of the kitchen and a TV (mainly used for traffic updates). Walls are decorated with some great black and white pictures of old trucks.

Meals are all fantastic value for money; all the usual truckstop fare like Yorkshire pudding, sausage, onion, peas, chips and gravy for £4.40 or Cornish pasties with peas, beans, chips, bread and butter £3.00.

OPENING TIMES

Mon-Fri:	07.00 - 19.00
Sat-Sun:	Closed
Public holidays:	Closed

FACILITIES

Parking: cars/trucks: plenty
Caravans/coaches welcome

FOOD AND DRINK

Daily specials
Kids' menu
Vegetarian menu
No alcoholic beverages

No credit cards

Willowtree Service Station

Willowtree Industrial Estate, Alnwick NE66 2HA
Tel: 01665 602641 Tel/Fax: 01665 602619 Email: ords.alnwick@alncom.net
Directions: Off A1 take road into Alnwick town. At first roundabout,
Willowtree Café is part of BP Service Station.

This small, purpose-built café is close to the picturesque town of Alnwick. It has its own entrance at the rear, or you can reach it through the service station. Costa coffee, as well as delicious pastries, buns and cakes, is on sale at the servery bar.

A daily menu of good-value meals includes steak slice sandwich at £1.79, plus the usual breakfasts at £3.99, and a daily special. Outside is a quiet eating area with tables where people can picnic. Cold drinks, ice creams, sweets and newspapers are sold in the service station shop.

There is parking for one coach only, so phone in advance to give arrival time.

Owned by Ords of Alnwick Ltd, the Willowtree is a quick stop on the way north to Edinburgh or south to Newcastle. As the Alnwick Castle Gardens become more popular, the café is becoming a convenient meeting place off the A1.

OPENING TIMES
Mon-Sun;
Public holidays: 09.00 - 17.00

FACILITIES
Disabled facilities
Cash machine: in service station nearby
Parking: cars: 10; trucks: 5
Caravans welcome
Coaches: one at a time
Garden

FOOD AND DRINK
Seating: 20
Outdoor eating area
Daily specials
Vegetarian menu
No alcoholic beverages

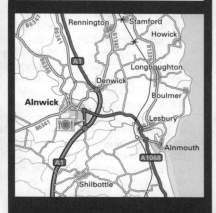

Index By Establishment Name

Location Index